Table of Contents

Using this Guide

This book is a *guide* for teachers using the *Primary Mathematics* curriculum. It is designed to help teachers understand the course material, see how each section fits in with the curriculum as a whole, and prepare the day's lesson. The course material is divided up into 80 sessions with one or two "activities" for each section. The second activity is an optional game or other group activity that can also be done during sessions or in any later session for review. Sessions can be combined for one day's lesson by spending less time on class participation or discussion or not having as many problems for practice during class time.

This guide is designed to be used with both the U.S. edition and the third edition of *Primary Mathematics*. U.S. conventions and spellings are used in this guide, such as using commas for thousands and colons for time, and not using "and" in writing out whole numbers in words. However, any items specific to either edition, such as different answers, different page numbers, and different exercise numbers, are clearly indicated, sometimes with a superscript **US** or **3d**.

This guide includes some worksheets, which can be copied for single class use only.

Workbook exercises can be gone over in class or assigned as homework.

Suggested Material

Counters
   Use some kind of counters that can be displayed, such as transparent counters with an overhead projector or something that can be stuck on the board and moved around. Students will also need counters of different colors for some of the games.

Number discs
   These are discs with 0.001, 0.01, 0.1, 1, 10, and 100 written on them. Have some that can be displayed; you can write the numbers on transparent counters if you have an overhead projector. You can also simply draw circles on the board and label them. For student manipulatives, you can write the numbers on opaque counters. Each student or group of students should have 18 of each type.

Hundreds board
   This is a chart with squares in a 10 x 10 array numbered from 1 to 100. Have one that can be displayed, such as one for the overhead projector, or one drawn on the board. You will also need to display a blank hundreds board, or a 10 x 10 array but without numbers in the squares. Each student should have a laminated or paper hundreds board with spaces large enough to be covered up by counters.

Base-10 blocks
   A set with unit cubes, rods (10 units), flats (10 rods), and a cube (10 flats). Use ones that can be displayed from the front of the class (such as using an overhead projector or ones that can be stuck onto the board). You can also just draw them on the board.

Number cubes
   This is a cube that can be labeled with different numbers. You need enough for each group of students to have 4 number cubes. 10-sided dice could also be used.

Number cards

Various number cards for games or group activities, see materials list for each part. You can use index cards, but make sure that the number does not show through the card. Many activities will call for four sets of number cards 0-9 for each group. (These can be made from playing cards by removing the face cards, making the Ace a 1, and whiting out the 1 and the symbols for the 10 to make them 0.)

Connect-a-cubes

These cubes can be connected on all six sides. There should be enough for each group of student to have about 100. Geo shapes are available that can also be connected to each other and to the cubes and are used in some optional activities.

Money

Use coins and bills up through $10 bills. Have ones that can be displayed, such as with an overhead projector, and play money that students can use to count and make change.

Store cards

These are teacher-made cards with a picture of an item and a cost for the item of less than $10, in increments of 5 cents.

Fraction circles, squares

You will need sets of circles and squares that show the whole and fractional parts. Use overhead fraction circles and squares or ones that can be displayed on the board.

Clock

Demonstration clock with geared hands and individual clocks with geared hands for each student.

Measuring tools

Rulers, quart/liter measuring cup or beaker. US: liquid measuring set with cup, pint, quart, half-gallon and gallon measuring cups or jars.

3-dimensional shapes

Models of cubes, cuboids (rectangular prism), cylinders, cones, and triangular prisms.

Optional Resources

Supplemental Workbooks

These optional workbooks provide a source of extra problems for more practice, tests, and class discussions. Some have interesting and thought-provoking non-routine problems for discussion.

Extra Practice for Primary Mathematics 2 (U.S. Edition)

This workbook has two to four page exercises covering topics from *Primary Mathematics 2A* and *Primary Mathematics 2B*. The level of difficulty and format of the problems is similar to that of the *Primary Mathematics*. Answers are in the back.

Primary Mathematics Challenging Word Problems 2 (U.S. Edition)
This workbook has word problems only. The problems are topically arranged, with the topics following the same sequence as *Primary Mathematics 2A* and *2B*. Each topic starts with three worked examples, followed by practice problems and then challenge problems. Although the computation skills needed to solve the problems is at the same level as the corresponding *Primary Mathematics*, the problem solving techniques necessary in the challenge section are sometimes more advanced, and the problems sometimes require more than one step to solve. It is a good source, though, of extra word problems that can be discussed in class or of enrichment problems for more capable students. Answers are in the back.

Primary Mathematics Intensive Practice 2B (U.S. Edition)
This supplemental workbook has one set of problems for each topic in *Primary Mathematics*. Each topical exercise has questions of varying levels of difficulty, but the difficulty level is usually higher than that in the *Primary Mathematics* textbook or workbook. Some of the word problems are quite challenging and require the students to extend their understanding of the concepts and to develop problem solving abilities. There is also a section called "Take the Challenge!" with non-routine problems that can be used to further develop students' problem solving abilities. Answers are located in the back.

Rainbow Rock CD-ROM
Rainbow Rock CD-ROM won the Bronze World Medal in the 1999 New York Festivals International Interactive Multimedia Competition in the Educational and Computer Science category. The setting is a prehistoric "Flintstone" type of world, with modern conveniences. Topics covered include material from both *Primary Mathematics 1* and *2*. Each grade level has two games and several learning areas to explore.

Primary Mathematics 2B		*Rainbow Rock Primary Two*
Unit 1 – Addition and Subtraction	Part 1 – Finding the Missing Number	Hundreds, Tens and Ones Challenge
Unit 2 – Multiplication and Division	Part 2 – Identifying Solid Figures	Multiplication Challenge Division Challenges 1-2
Review A		Word Problems Learn and Explore 3 Learn and Explore 4 Activity Challenge Came 1 – Levels 5-9
Unit 4 – Fractions	Part 2 – Writing Fractions	Fractions Learn and Explore Activity Challenges 1-2
Unit 8 – Geometry	Part 1 – Flat and Curved Faces	Shapes Learn and Explore
	Part 2 – Making Shapes	Shapes Activities Challenges 1-3

Unit 1 – Addition and Subtraction

Objectives

- Find the missing number in addition and subtraction equations.
- Use mental calculation strategies to subtract from 100.
- Use mental calculation strategies for addition.
- Use mental calculation strategies for subtraction.

Suggested number of sessions: 13

	Objectives	Textbook	Workbook	Activity
Part 1 : Finding the Missing Number				**4 sessions**
1	▪ Find the missing part in an addition or subtraction equation.	pp. 6-7 pp. 7-8, tasks 1-2(a)		1.1a
2	▪ Find the missing whole in a subtraction equation.	pp. 8-9, tasks 2(b)-3	Ex. 1	1.1b
3	▪ Use the count-on strategy to "make 100". ▪ Use the missing number strategy to "make 100". ▪ Make 100. ▪ Mentally subtract from 100.	pp. 9-10, tasks 4-7	Ex. 2	1.1c
4	▪ Practice.	p. 11, Practice 1A		1.1d
Part 2 : Methods for Mental Addition				**4 sessions**
5	▪ Add ones or tens to a 3-digit number.	p. 13, task 1	Ex. 3	1.2a 1.2b
6	▪ Add ones, tens, or hundreds to a 3-digit number.	p. 12, p. 13, task 2	Ex. 4	1.2c 1.2d
7	▪ Add two 2-digit numbers.	p. 13, tasks 3-4	Ex. 5	1.2e 1.2f
8	▪ Add 99 or 98 to a 1-digit or 2-digit number. ▪ Add 99 or 98 to a 3-digit number.	p. 14, tasks 5-9	Ex. 6 Ex. 7	1.2g 1.2h
Part 3 : Methods for Mental Subtraction				**5 sessions**
9	▪ Subtract ones or tens from a 2-digit number.	p. 16, task 1	Ex. 8	1.3a
10	▪ Subtract ones, tens, or hundreds from a 3-digit number.	p. 15, p. 16, task 2	Ex. 9	1.3b 1.3c
11	▪ Subtract 2-digit numbers.	p. 15, tasks 3-4	Ex. 10	1.3d 1.3e
12	▪ Subtract 99 or 98 from hundreds. ▪ Subtract 99 or 98 from a 3-digit numbers.	p. 17, tasks 5-9 p. 17, tasks 7-9	Ex. 11 Ex. 12	1.3f 1.3g
13	▪ Practice (using both mental strategies and the addition and subtraction algorithms).	p. 18, Practice 1B p. 19, Practice 1C	Review 1	1.3h

| **Part 1: Finding the Missing Number (pp. 6-11)** | **4 sessions** |

Objectives

- Find the missing number in an addition or subtraction equation.
- Find the number to "make 100" with another number less than 100.

Materials

- Displayable counters
- Displayable number discs (discs with 1, 10, and 100 written on them)
- Blank displayable hundreds board
- Displayable base-10 blocks
- Set of 20 cards consisting of ten pairs of numbers whose sum is 100, one set per group
- Number cubes, 2 per group, one labeled with 1-6 and the other with 4-9
- Number cards 0-9, 4 sets per group

Homework

- Workbook Exercise 1
- Workbook Exercise 2

Notes

In this part, students will use the part-whole concept to find a missing number in an addition or subtraction equation.

When we know the parts, we use **addition** to find the whole. This can be represented as a number bond with a missing total.

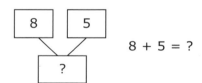

This can also be represented pictorially.

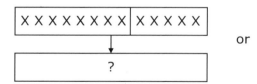   or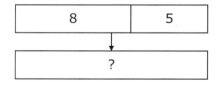

When we know the whole and one of the parts of the whole, we use **subtraction** to find the missing part. This can be represented as a number bond with a missing part.

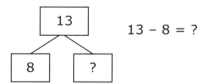

This can also be represented pictorially:

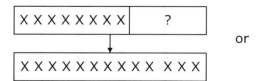   or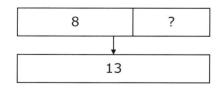

Students will use the part-whole concept to find a missing number in addition and subtraction equations:

- In the equation **? + 8 = 13** the missing number represents an unknown part. The unknown part can therefore be found by subtraction: **13 − 8 = ?.**

- In the equation **13 - ? = 8** the whole is given, an unknown part is removed, leaving a known part. Since we have a whole and a known part, the unknown part can be found by subtraction: **13 − 8 = ?.**

- In the equation **? - 8 = 5**, the whole is unknown. When one part is subtracted from the whole, the result is the other part. Since we have two parts, the unknown whole can be found by addition: **8 + 5 = ?.**

Students can solve missing number problems using mental calculations or the addition or subtraction algorithm. The addition and subtraction algorithms were learned in *Primary Mathematics 2A* and involve rewriting the problem vertically and adding or subtracting first the ones, then the tens, then the hundreds, renaming where necessary.

Students will learn two mental strategies for finding the missing part when the total is 100, or for "making 100."

$$68 + \boxed{?} = 100$$

Students can count on, first by ones to the next ten and then by tens, or first by tens and then by ones:

$$68 \xrightarrow{+2} 70 \xrightarrow{+30} 100$$

$$68 \xrightarrow{+30} 98 \xrightarrow{+2} 100$$

They can also use the knowledge that 100 is 9 tens and 10 ones.

$$68 \begin{cases} 60 + \boxed{30} = 90 \\ 8 + \boxed{2} = 10 \end{cases} 100$$

$$68 \quad + \quad \boxed{32} = 100$$

The skills needed to solve the word problems in this unit were covered in *Primary Mathematics 2A*. If necessary, refer back to the Teacher's Guide for that level for teaching strategies.

Activity 1.1a   **Missing number**

1. Illustrate a part-whole situation which has a missing part.
    *   Use counters or other objects to display two parts and the whole.

    *   Draw the number bond. Point out the two parts and the whole.

    *   Remove or cover up one of the parts. Ask students for the equation to find the missing part. (11 − 7 = ?)

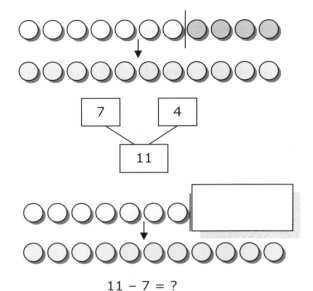

$$11 - 7 = ?$$

    *   Write the related addition equation with a missing number. Have the students relate each part of this equation to the objects. The missing part is the covered part. With this equation we have one known part, an unknown part, and a known total. We can find the missing part by subtraction.

$$7 + \boxed{?} = 11 \longleftrightarrow 11 - 7 = \boxed{?}$$

    *   Cover up the counters in the other part and rewrite the equation to show a different missing part. Show how the missing part for this new equation can also be found by subtraction.
    *   Students should not be required to rewrite the problem as a subtraction equation if they can find the missing number mentally.

$$\boxed{?} + 4 = 11 \longleftrightarrow 11 - 4 = \boxed{?}$$

    *   Discuss **text pp. 6-7.**
    *   Repeat with other examples where the total is more than 20 but less than 100. You can illustrate with bars or number bonds. Allow students to solve the problems either mentally or by writing the related subtraction problem vertically and solving it using renaming, as was learned in *Primary Mathematics 2A*. Some students may be able to solve problems involving 2-digit numbers by counting on. For example, they can solve 23 + ? = 37 by thinking "23 to 33 is 10, 33 to 37 is 4, the missing number is 14."

$$23 + \boxed{?} = 37 \longleftrightarrow 37 - 23 = \boxed{?}$$

$$\boxed{?} + 42 = 60 \longleftrightarrow 60 - 42 = \boxed{?}$$

- Provide some examples where the whole is between 100 and 1000. Students can use the subtraction algorithm to solve these.

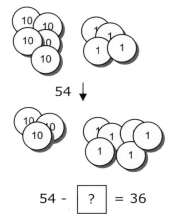

$$82 + \boxed{?} = 343 \longleftrightarrow 343 - 82 = \boxed{?}$$

$$\begin{array}{r} 3\,4\,3 \\ -\ \ 8\,2 \\ \hline 2\,6\,1 \end{array}$$

2. Illustrate a part-whole situation where an unknown amount is taken away from a known amount, leaving a known amount.
   - Use number discs. Display some amount less than 100, such as 54. Write down 54. Tell students that we have a total of 54.

   - Tell students that some are taken away, but we don't know how many. We do know 36 are left.
   - Remove all the discs and replace with 36.
   - Add "– ? = 36" to the equation.

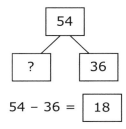

$$54 - \boxed{?} = 36$$

   - Write the boxes for a number bond.
   - Remind students that we started with 54. Write 54 in the box for the whole. We took away one part and are left with the other part. Write ? in one of the part boxes and 36 in the other.
   - Ask students how we find a missing part. From the whole (54), we subtract the part that was left (36) to find the part that was taken away (?).
   - Write the related equation and ask for the answer. Write the original equation with the missing number included.

$$54 - 36 = \boxed{18}$$

$$54 - \boxed{18} = 36$$

   - Discuss **tasks 1-2(b), text pp. 7-8.**

3. Provide other addition and subtraction problems with a missing part for practice. Students can work on them individually or in groups.

Activity 1.1b

Missing whole

1. Illustrate a subtraction situation where we know what is taken away, we know what is left, but we don't know the whole.
   - Use number discs. Display an amount between 10 and 100, such as 33, in a pile so that it is not possible to determine the exact number. Cover with a piece of paper or index card. Tell students you have a certain number of items.
   - Pull out a part, such as 12, from under the paper or card. Tell students you took away 12. Set the 12 off to the side. Write "? - 12" on the board.
   - Remove the paper covering the remainder and separate tens and ones. Show that 21 is left. Add "= 21" to the number sentence.
   - Write the boxes for a number bond.
   - Ask students what goes into each box. Write ? in the box for total, and 12 and 21 in the boxes for parts.
   - Ask students how we can find the total. We add.
   - Write the related equation and ask students for the answer. Use that answer in the original equation.

2. Discuss **tasks 2.(c) – 3, text p. 9**.
   - In task 3, students should tell you whether they need to find the sum or difference of the known numbers to determine the unknown number.
   - Allow them to solve the problems mentally if they can. Otherwise, they can write the related equation vertically and solve using the addition or subtraction algorithm.

3. Provide some additional problems for practice.
   - Provide other problems for individual or group practice. Provide problems of all three types.
   - Allow students to solve the problems mentally if they can.
   - Include some problems involving 3-digit numbers where they can review the addition and subtraction algorithms.

Workbook Exercise 1

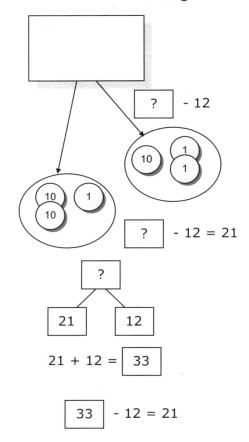

Part + ? = Whole
Whole - ? = Part
? – Part = Part

Activity 1.1c   **Make 100**

1. Illustrate the process of "making 100" by counting on.

    *   Write a missing number equation with a sum of 100 such as 52 + ___ = 100, and a corresponding number bond.

    *   Color in the corresponding number of squares on a hundreds board with blank squares.

    *   Color in the rest of the squares in a column with a second color, and then the rest of the columns with a third color, to show that the missing number can be found by adding 8 to get to the next ten, and then 40 to get to 100.
    *   Ask students for other methods. They could also see they can add 4 tens (40) to get to 92 and then add 8 to get to 100.

2. Illustrate the process of "making 100" by finding the missing tens and ones:
    *   Use another blank hundreds board or erase and color in the corresponding number of squares again, but this time so that the partial column is the last column.

    *   Point to the first 9 columns and then individually to the last 10 squares. Remind your students that 100 is the same as 9 tens plus 10 ones. Write on the board as illustrated on the right.
    *   Tell them we need 4 more tens to get to 9 tens and 8 more ones to get to 10 ones. The missing number is 48.

$$52 + \boxed{?} = 100$$

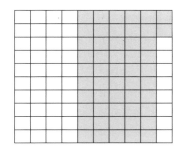

$$52 \xrightarrow{+8} 60 \xrightarrow{+40} 100$$

$$52 \xrightarrow{+40} 92 \xrightarrow{+8} 100$$

$$52 + \boxed{48} = 100$$

$$52 \begin{cases} 50 + \boxed{40} = 90 \\ 2 + \boxed{8} = 10 \end{cases} 100$$

- Repeat with another problem. Write it as a subtraction problem this time rather than a missing number problem.

  o Write the problem 100 – 34 = _____. Color the corresponding number of squares on the hundreds chart.

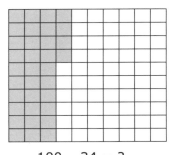

  o Have students count on to find the answer.

$$100 - 34 = ?$$

$$34 \xrightarrow{\ +6\ } 40 \xrightarrow{\ +60\ } 100$$

$$34 \xrightarrow{\ +60\ } 94 \xrightarrow{\ +6\ } 100$$

$$100 - 34 = 66$$

  o Then have them find the answer by making 9 with the tens and making 10 with the ones.

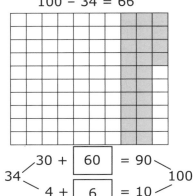

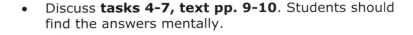

- Discuss **tasks 4-7, text pp. 9-10**. Students should find the answers mentally.

Activity 1.1d   **Practice and word problems**

1. Have students do **problems 1-2, Practice 1A, text p. 11**.

2. Use **problems 3-5, Practice 1A, text p. 11** to review word problems.
   - Discuss these problems in terms of the part-whole concept. Ask students to determine whether two parts are given and the whole must be found, or whether the whole and one part are given and a missing part must be found. Have students draw a number bond and then write an equation.
   - For example, in #3, the total is the number of ducks. The farmer gives away one part, and has one part left. We could write the equation 215 - ____ = 36, or we could write 215 – 36 = _____ for whole – part = part.

3. Divide students into groups. Do one or more of the following activities.
   - Provide each group with a set of 20 cards consisting of ten pairs of numbers whose sum is 100. Cards are shuffled and placed face up in the middle. Students take turns choosing 2 cards that make 100.
   - Provide each group with two number cubes, one labeled 1-6 and the other 4-9. Students take turns with rolling the cubes, forming a 2-digit number from the rolled number, and then giving the number that makes 100 with it.
   - Provide each group with 4 sets of number cards 0-9. Shuffle the cards and place face down in the middle. Students take turns drawing two cards, forming a 2-digit number with them, and then giving the number that makes 100 with it.
   - Have students do Mental Math 1 and 2 on the next two pages.

Mental Math 1

1. $100 - 20 =$ _____

2. $100 - 75 =$ _____

3. $100 - 7 =$ _____

4. $100 - 98 =$ _____

5. $100 - 6 =$ _____

6. $100 - 35 =$ _____

7. $100 - 48 =$ _____

8. $100 - 25 =$ _____

9. $100 - 46 =$ _____

10. $100 - 10 =$ _____

11. $100 - 77 =$ _____

12. $100 - 12 =$ _____

13. $100 - 5 =$ _____

14. $100 - 29 =$ _____

15. $100 - 33 =$ _____

16. $32 +$ _____ $= 100$

17. $71 +$ _____ $= 100$

18. $57 +$ _____ $= 100$

19. $60 +$ _____ $= 100$

20. _____ $+ 40 = 100$

21. _____ $+ 35 = 100$

22. _____ $+ 3 = 100$

23. _____ $+ 22 = 100$

24. $100 -$ _____ $= 50$

25. $100 -$ _____ $= 61$

26. $100 -$ _____ $= 84$

27. $100 -$ _____ $= 53$

28. $100 -$ _____ $= 38$

29. $100 -$ _____ $= 79$

30. $100 -$ _____ $= 9$

Mental Math 2

1. $100 - 75 =$ _____

2. $100 - 30 =$ _____

3. $65 +$ _____ $= 100$

4. _____ $+ 23 = 100$

5. _____ $+ 85 = 100$

6. $100 - 80 =$ _____

7. $48 +$ _____ $= 100$

8. $100 - 22 =$ _____

9. $100 -$ _____ $= 8$

10. $100 - 19 =$ _____

11. $100 - 64 =$ _____

12. $100 -$ _____ $= 91$

13. _____ $+ 44 = 100$

14. $74 +$ _____ $= 100$

15. _____ $+ 31 = 100$

16. $100 - 35 =$ _____

17. $25 +$ _____ $= 100$

18. $100 - 40 =$ _____

19. $6 +$ _____ $= 100$

20. _____ $+ 10 = 100$

21. $100 - 15 =$ _____

22. $100 - 62 =$ _____

23. _____ $+ 36 = 100$

24. $100 -$ _____ $= 25$

25. $100 - 81 =$ _____

26. $75 + 25 =$ _____

27. $75 + 25 + 94 =$ _____

28. $68 + 21 + 32 =$ _____

29. $54 + 46 +$ _____ $= 134$

30. $47 + 75 +$ _____ $= 147$

Part 2: Methods for Mental Addition (pp. 12-14)	**4 sessions**

Objectives

- Add ones or tens to a 2-digit number.
- Add ones, tens, or hundreds to a 3-digit number.
- Add two 2-digit numbers.
- Add 99 or 98.

Materials

- Displayable number discs (1, 10, and 100)
- Displayable base-10 blocks, including a copy of one 100-flat with two squares cut out, or with 98 squares colored in
- Worksheets with additional problems (see activity 1.2b)
- Number cards, 1-9 and the tens 10-90, 1 or 2 sets per group
- Number cards, 0-9, 4 sets per group, plus six more 0's per group
- Hundreds board and counters for each group
- Number cubes, 4 per group

Homework

- Workbook Exercise 4
- Workbook Exercise 5
- Workbook Exercise 6
- Workbook Exercise 7

Notes

Mental Math strategies are reviewed here, and new ones are introduced. Some students may be using some of the new strategies already based on their own experience.

Learning and using mental calculation strategies encourages flexibility in thinking about numbers and helps the student develop a strong number sense. Flexibility is a key here. Though the students are taught strategies, they should be encouraged to develop, utilize, and share their own strategies.

The following strategies will be reviewed or taught here. The number bond illustrations are included here to help make the strategies clearer with respect to place values to you as the teacher — students may draw number bonds if needed but eventually they should be able to add mentally without writing out the number bonds.

➢ Add 1, 2, or 3 by counting on.
   59 + 2 = 61; count on 60, 61.
   338 + 3 = 341; count on 339, 340, 341

➢ Add a 1-digit number to a 2-digit or 3-digit number without renaming by adding ones to ones.
   155 + 4 = 159

   $155 + 4 = 150 + 9 = 159$
   150   5

➢ Add 10, 20, or 30 by counting on.
   288 + 30 = 318; count up 298, 308, 318 (or count tens first then add ones: 29, 30, 31 tens, 318.

➤ Add tens to each other without renaming by adding the tens.
   150 + 30 = 180

➤ Add tens to a 2-digit or 3-digit number without renaming by adding to the tens.
   155 + 40 = 195

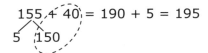
155 + 40 = 190 + 5 = 195
5   150

➤ Add a 1-digit number to a 2-digit or 3-digit number by making a 10:
   176 + 8 = 184

176 + 8 = 180 + 4 = 184
4   4

➤ Add a 1-digit number to a 2-digit or 3-digit number by recalling the addition fact and renaming ten ones as a ten.
   176 + 8 = 184

176 + 8 = 170 + 14 = 184
170   6

➤ Add tens to a 2-digit or 3-digit number by adding the tens using the same strategies as for adding ones.
   283 + 70 = 353 (28 + 7 = 35, so 280 + 70 = 350, add ones, 353)

➤ Add hundreds to a 3-digit number by adding hundreds to hundreds.
   234 + 500 = 734

234 + 500 = 700 + 34 = 734
34   200

➤ Add two 2-digit numbers by first adding the tens and then the ones.
   53 + 34 = 53 + 30 + 4 = 83 + 4 = 87

➤ Add a number close to 100 by making 100. (This is the method shown in the text.)
   457 + 98 = 555

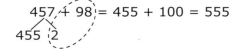
457 + 98 = 455 + 100 = 555
455   2

➤ Add a number close to 100 by first adding 100 and then subtracting the difference. (This is easier to do than making 100.)
   457 + 98 = 457 + 100 – 2 = 557 – 2 = 555

Some students may be able to extend the strategies given in this section or derive other strategies. Do not discourage your students' attempts to manipulate numbers. Do not require the students to write down their steps, or explain their steps in writing. This negates the usefulness of mental math. Encourage them to share their ideas and methods orally. If a student gives a wrong answer, help him or her to go through his process step by step to try to find the error. However, do not require students to use mental calculations in problems where they are more comfortable using the addition algorithm. Students should find out for themselves when and where to try mental math, and also when it is safer for them to stick to the standard addition algorithm. Students may also add by drawing number bonds rather than doing the problem mentally if they need to.

Activity 1.2a   **Add ones or tens**

1. Illustrate the addition of ones to a 2-digit number. Use number discs.
    *   Display 5 tens and 4 ones. Add 8 more ones next to them. Write the expression 54 + 8 and discuss strategies to mentally find the value of 54 + 8. Explain that in using mental strategies we often start at the highest place value.

        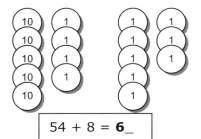

        $$54 + 8 = \mathbf{6\_}$$

        o   Find the tens: Before determining the tens for the answer, look to the ones. Will the ones increase the tens? Yes, so add 1 to the tens. The tens of the sum will be 6. Write 6 for the tens.
        o   Find the ones: Discuss two methods.

        1. Use the addition fact (4 + 8 = 12). This tells us there are 2 ones. To show this, move the 4 ones over to the right with the other ones, then change 10 ones for a ten. You can also draw a number bond picture.

            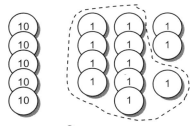

            $$54 + 8 = 50 + 12 = 62$$

            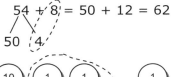

        2. Make a ten (54 takes 6 from 8 to make 60, there are 2 left over). Show this by moving 6 of the ones over towards the 54, and then changing 10 ones for a ten. You can also draw a number bond.

            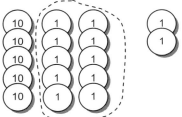

            $$54 + 8 = 60 + 2 = 62$$

            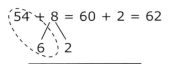

            $$54 + 8 = 6\mathbf{2}$$

        Write 2 for the ones.

    *   Write the expression 29 + 2.
        o   Tell students that if they are adding a small number such as 1, 2, or 3, they can simply count on: 30, 31. $$29 + 2 = 31$$
        o   Students should realize that when counting on from 29 they do not include 29.
    *   Write the expression 55 + 4. $$55 + 4 = 59$$
        o   Ask students to look at the ones. 5 and 4 are not enough to make another ten.
        o   The tens digit stays the same, and the ones are simply added together.
    *   Write some other problems on the board involving addition of ones to a 2-digit number, particularly problems where there is renaming in the ones, and have the students find the answers mentally. Ask them what strategy they used.

3. Illustrate the addition of tens to a 2-digit number. Use number discs.
   - Display 4 tens and 5 ones. Add 8 more tens next to them. Write the expression 45 + 80.

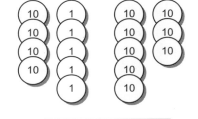

   - ○ Add the tens. We can add the tens by just adding the digits. Since 4 + 8 = 12, then 4 tens + 8 tens = 12 tens. Write 12 tens.
   - ○ Find the ones: The ones are just the 5 from 45. Write 5 down for ones.
   - ○ You can show the process with number bonds.

$$45 + 80 = \mathbf{12}\_$$

$$45 + 80 = 12\mathbf{5}$$

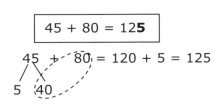

$$45 + 80 = 120 + 5 = 125$$

   - Write the expression 91 + 20.
     - ○ Tell students that if they are adding 10, 20, or 30, they can simply count on by tens: 101, 111.

$$91 + 20 = 111$$

   - Write a few other problems on the board involving addition of tens to a 2-digit number, particularly problems where there is renaming in the tens, and have the students find the answers mentally. Ask them what strategy they used.

4. Have students do **task 1, text p. 13**.
   - You can use Mental Math 3 and 4 on the next two pages for additional practice, now or later.

Workbook Exercise 3

Activity 1.2b   **Sprint**

1. The following activity can be used with other types of computation practice, such as memorizing multiplication and division facts later.
   - Provide students with a worksheet containing at least 10 or more problems similar to task 1 in the text, p. 13. Hand out the papers face-down.
   - Use a stopwatch. Tell them to start. They turn their papers over and answer the problems. Students raise their hands when done. When about half are done tell them to stop and stop the timer. Tell students the time.
   - Go through the problems one by one. Call out the answers and ask those students who got the problem right to raise their hands. The students will be encouraged by getting some right answers, and won't mind as much not getting all of them.
   - This activity can be called a **sprint**. If you give this activity once or twice a week, students can compete with themselves and try to finish more problems in the short time given. You can give them a set amount of time rather than waiting until half are finished.

Mental Math 3

1.   24 + 3 = _____

2.   62 + 5 = _____

3.   44 + 6 = _____

4.   59 + 6 = _____

5.   26 + 7 = _____

6.   25 + 4 = _____

7.   64 + 8 = _____

8.   77 + 4 = _____

9.   71 + 7 = _____

10.   35 + 7 = _____

11.   27 + 8 = _____

12.   35 + 3 = _____

13.   56 + 4 = _____

14.   22 + 6 = _____

15.   26 + 6 = _____

16.   86 + 3 = _____

17.   59 + 8 = _____

18.   38 + 3 = _____

19.   79 + 7 = _____

20.   28 + 2 = _____

21.   17 + 7 = _____

22.   19 + 8 = _____

23.   73 + 4 = _____

24.   18 + 2 = _____

25.   59 + 9 = _____

26.   36 + 3 = _____

27.   54 + 8 = _____

28.   13 + 5 = _____

29.   82 + 9 = _____

30.   93 + 7 = _____

Mental Math 4

1.   11 + 80 = _____

2.   62 + 20 = _____

3.   78 + 20 = _____

4.   42 + 10 = _____

5.   98 + 20 = _____

6.   12 + 50 = _____

7.   34 + 90 = _____

8.   86 + 40 = _____

9.   32 + 40 = _____

10. 52 + 50 = _____

11. 67 + 70 = _____

12. 32 + 40 = _____

13. 80 + 80 = _____

14. 78 + 20 = _____

15. 38 + 40 = _____

16. 27 + 50 = _____

17. 60 + 60 = _____

18. 70 + 40 = _____

19. 15 + 30 = _____

20. 56 + 80 = _____

21. 77 + 50 = _____

22. 32 + 90 = _____

23. 33 + 50 = _____

24. 90 + 60 = _____

25. 80 + 70 = _____

26. 42 + 50 = _____

27. 50 + 50 = _____

28. 68 + 40 = _____

29. 24 + 60 = _____

30. 14 + 90 = _____

Activity 1.2c

1. Illustrate mental addition of ones, tens, or hundreds to a 3-digit number without renaming.
   - Use number discs. Have your students look at the **text p. 12** as they follow the discussion. Display 3 hundreds, 5 tens, and 6 ones.
   - Display 2 more ones next to it and write the expression 356 + 2. Show that ones are added to ones. Point to the ones in the written number 356. Elicit the answer.
   - Replace the 2 ones with 2 tens. Write the expression 356 + 20. Show that tens are added to tens. Point to the tens in 356. Elicit the answer.
   - Replace the 2 tens with 2 hundreds. Write the expression 356 + 200. Show that hundreds are added to hundreds. Point to the hundreds in the number 356. Elicit the answer.

2. Illustrate mental addition of ones to a 3-digit number where there is renaming.
   - Start with the original 3 hundreds, 5 tens, and 6 ones. Display another 8 ones. Discuss strategies to mentally find the sum for 356 + 8.
     - Find the hundreds. Since we won't be adding tens, the hundreds stay the same. Write 3 for the hundreds.
     - Find 56 + 8 using the same strategies already discussed. Write down the tens and then the ones.
   - You can draw a number bond to illustrate the process.

3. Illustrate mental addition of tens to a 3-digit number where there is renaming.
   - Start with the original 3 hundreds, 5 tens, and 6 ones. Display another 8 tens. Discuss strategies to mentally find the sum for 356 + 80.
     - Tell students that since we are adding tens, we can ignore the ones for now.
     - 350 is 35 tens. We can add 35 tens and 8 tens using the same strategies for adding 35 ones and 8 ones. Ask for the sum of 35 and 8 (35 + 8 = 43).
     - If 35 + 8 = 43, then 35 tens + 8 tens = 43 tens. Write down 43 tens.
     - Find the ones. The ones will just be the 6 from 356. Write 6 down for the ones.

Add ones, tens, or hundreds

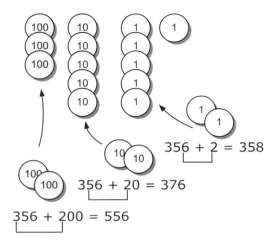

$$356 + 2 = 358$$
$$356 + 20 = 376$$
$$356 + 200 = 556$$

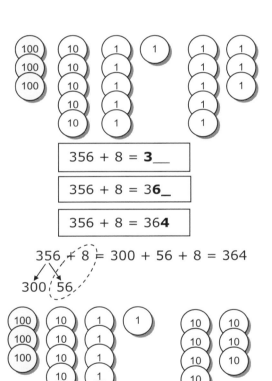

| $356 + 8 = \mathbf{3}\_\_$ |
| $356 + 8 = 3\mathbf{6}\_$ |
| $356 + 8 = 36\mathbf{4}$ |

$$356 + 8 = 300 + 56 + 8 = 364$$
300 56

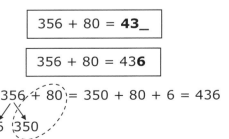

| $356 + 80 = \mathbf{43}\_$ |
| $356 + 80 = 43\mathbf{6}$ |

$$356 + 80 = 350 + 80 + 6 = 436$$
6 350

- Write the expression 479 + 30. Explain that with smaller tens we can count up: 48 tens, 49 tens, 50 tens, so the answer is 50 tens and nine, or 509.

$$479 + 30 = 509$$

4. Have students do **task 2, text p. 13**.
   - You can use the Mental Math 5 and 6 on the next two pages for additional practice, now or later.

Workbook Exercise 4

Activity 1.2d   **Practice**

Material for each group of students:
- Number cards 1-9 and 10, 20, 30, 40, 50, 60, 70, 80, and 90.
- Paper with 2 columns, labeled as shown on the right, with 100 in the *Total* column, one sheet for each student.

Add	Total
	100

Procedure:
- Cards are shuffled and placed face-down in the middle.
- Students take turns turning over a card and writing the number in the *Add* column. That student mentally adds the number (e.g. 40) to the previous total (100) and writes the new total (140) under the previous total.
- If the group agrees that the addition is correct, the old total is crossed out and the next student chooses a card, such as 2.
- All students can fill out one chart, using the numbers for each students turn. If there is adequate time, or if this activity is done later when there is more time, students can fill out charts with only their own numbers.
- Play continues until each group or student reaches 900. Cards are reshuffled when needed.

Add	Total
	100
40	140
2	142
80	222

Mental Math 5

1. $412 + 5 =$ _____

2. $626 + 4 =$ _____

3. $322 + 6 =$ _____

4. $909 + 3 =$ _____

5. $811 + 5 =$ _____

6. $303 + 7 =$ _____

7. $105 + 8 =$ _____

8. $716 + 4 =$ _____

9. $841 + 9 =$ _____

10. $384 + 7 =$ _____

11. $147 + 7 =$ _____

12. $254 + 8 =$ _____

13. $782 + 5 =$ _____

14. $388 + 7 =$ _____

15. $103 + 7 =$ _____

16. $615 + 8 =$ _____

17. $867 + 6 =$ _____

18. $855 + 9 =$ _____

19. $152 + 8 =$ _____

20. $492 + 5 =$ _____

21. $808 + 5 =$ _____

22. $219 + 6 =$ _____

23. $628 + 2 =$ _____

24. $247 + 7 =$ _____

25. $877 + 6 =$ _____

26. $203 + 7 =$ _____

27. $318 + 5 =$ _____

28. $121 + 9 =$ _____

29. $179 + 4 =$ _____

30. $394 + 6 =$ _____

Mental Math 6

1. $484 + 10 = $ _____	16. $655 + 80 = $ _____
2. $728 + 40 = $ _____	17. $878 + 60 = $ _____
3. $460 + 60 = $ _____	18. $587 + 70 = $ _____
4. $312 + 70 = $ _____	19. $131 + 80 = $ _____
5. $677 + 20 = $ _____	20. $399 + 50 = $ _____
6. $321 + 20 = $ _____	21. $470 + 200 = $ _____
7. $541 + 50 = $ _____	22. $312 + 260 = $ _____
8. $229 + 60 = $ _____	23. $569 + 300 = $ _____
9. $350 + 70 = $ _____	24. $181 + 800 = $ _____
10. $462 + 50 = $ _____	25. $752 + 200 = $ _____
11. $877 + 70 = $ _____	26. $271 + 600 = $ _____
12. $245 + 80 = $ _____	27. $358 + 200 = $ _____
13. $384 + 80 = $ _____	28. $167 + 800 = $ _____
14. $590 + 70 = $ _____	29. $56 + 500 = $ _____
15. $209 + 30 = $ _____	30. $673 + 400 = $ _____

Activity 1.2e   **Add 2-digit numbers**

1. Illustrate mental addition of 2-digit numbers.
   - Write the expression 36 + 45 on the board and
     display two corresponding sets of number discs.
   - Discuss methods to add these two numbers
     mentally:

     1. Find each digit from right to left:
        - Find the tens. Look ahead to the ones –
          will adding the ones increase the tens?
          Yes, so add the tens and increase the
          sum by 1. Write 8 for the tens.
        - Find the ones: 6 + 5 = 11, so the ones is
          1. Write 1 for the ones.
     2. Find an intermediate number.
        - Add the tens of the second number to the
          first number to get the intermediate sum
          76.
        - Add the ones to get the final sum. 76 + 5
          = 81.
   - Discuss **task 3, text p. 13**.

   36 + 45 = ?

   36 + 45 = **8**_

   36 + 45 = 8**1**

   $$36 \xrightarrow{+40} 76 \xrightarrow{+5} 81$$

   36 + 45 = 81

2. Have student provide answers for **task 4, text p. 13**.
   - Do some additional examples where there is renaming in the ones.

Workbook Exercise 5

Activity 1.2f   **Game**

Material for each group of about 4 students:
- Hundreds number board.
- Four sets of number cards 0-9 and 6 extra cards with 0.
- Counters, one color per student.

Procedure:
- Shuffle cards and place face-down in the center.
- All students draw 4 cards. They then arrange the cards into two 2-digit numbers. The
  sum of the numbers should be less than 100. If a 0 is drawn, it can be used for ones or
  discarded so one of the numbers will be a 1-digit number. For example, if 3, 4, 8 and 0
  are drawn, 8 cannot be used as a ten, because if either 3 or 4 is used as the other ten,
  then the sum will be greater than 100. Possible pairs of numbers are 34, 8 or 38, 40. If
  it is not possible to make two numbers whose sum is less than 100, the student discards
  the highest digit and redraws a card.
- As soon as the student has formed the two numbers and found the sum, he or she
  places a counter on the hundreds board to cover up an uncovered number
  corresponding to the sum. Play continues until a student has 3 counters in a row.

Activity 1.2g

Add 99 or 98 to a number

1. Illustrate addition of 98 and 99 to a 2-digit number.
   - Use displayable base-10 blocks. Use a 100-flat with 2 squares cut out or covered up for 98.
   - Write the expression 98 + 23 on the board.
     - Ask students how they can use the idea of making 100 to mentally add these two numbers.
     - Move 2 ones over from 23 to fill in the rest of the flat. This makes 100. Ask how many are left. 21 are left. So 98 + 23 = 100 + 21 = 121.
     - Remove the blocks and put back the 23. Then put up the grid with 2 squares missing representing 98. Write 23 + 98.
   - Replace the 98-grid with a full 10x10 grid. Ask how many more we would get if we added 100 instead of 98. There would be 2 too many. So we could get the same answer by adding 100 and then taking away 2.
   - Discuss **task 5, text p. 14**.
     - In this task, 1 is added to 99 to make 100. Ask students if they can do the problem another way.
     - Lead them to see they can add 100 to 4 to get 104, and then take away 1 to get 103. They add 100 and remove the difference.
   - Have students supply answers to **tasks 7-8, text p. 14**.

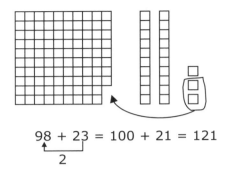

$$98 + 23 = 100 + 21 = 121$$
$$23 + 98 = 23 + 100 - 2 = 121$$

2. Illustrate addition of 98 and 99 to a 3-digit number.
   - Write the expression 121 + 98 on the board. Illustrate with base-10 blocks, using the one with 2 squares removed or covered. Discuss strategies for solving this problem mentally. Students can either make 100 with 98 by taking 2 from 121, or add 100 to 121 and then subtract 2.
   - Discuss **task 8, text p. 14**.
   - Have students supply answers to **task 9, text p. 14**.

3. You may want to extend the discussion to other numbers between 95 and 100, and to adding a number close to a multiple of 100.
   - Ask students how they would solve 345 + 97 or 345 + 95.
   - Ask students how they would solve 48 + 298 or 248 + 298. They could add 300 and then subtract 2.
   - Give students additional problems for practice. You can use Mental Math 7 on the next page.

Workbook Exercises 6 and 7

Activity 1.2h

Practice

Material for each group of about 4 students:
- One number cubes labeled with 0-5, one labeled with 5-9, and one labeled with 0, 2, 3, 5, 7, and 8 and one labeled with two each of 99, 98, and 97.

Procedure:
- Students take turns throwing the number cubes. They form a 1, 2 or 3-digit number (004 would be a 1-digit number) from the values on the cubes with single digits and add the number thrown on the cube with 99, 98, or 97. Other students check the answer.

Mental Math 7

1. $14 + 99 = $ _____

2. $35 + 98 = $ _____

3. $5 + 99 = $ _____

4. $33 + 98 = $ _____

5. $47 + 99 = $ _____

6. $24 + 99 = $ _____

7. $52 + 98 = $ _____

8. $70 + 99 = $ _____

9. $73 + 98 = $ _____

10. $14 + 99 = $ _____

11. $98 + 98 = $ _____

12. $526 + 98 = $ _____

13. $317 + 98 = $ _____

14. $640 + 99 = $ _____

15. $813 + 98 = $ _____

16. $98 + 417 = $ _____

17. $99 + 333 = $ _____

18. $268 + 98 = $ _____

19. $97 + 239 = $ _____

20. $98 + 506 = $ _____

21. $98 + 582 = $ _____

22. $181 + 99 = $ _____

23. $325 + 98 = $ _____

24. $97 + 592 = $ _____

25. $98 + 403 = $ _____

26. $35 + 97 = $ _____

27. $96 + 213 = $ _____

28. $199 + 25 = $ _____

29. $198 + 195 = $ _____

30. $429 + 298 = $ _____

Part 3: Methods for Mental Subtraction (pp. 15-19)	5 sessions

Objectives

* Subtract ones or tens from a 2-digit number.
* Subtract ones, tens, or hundreds from a 3-digit number.
* Subtract two 2-digit numbers.
* Subtract 99 or 98.

Materials

* Displayable number discs (1, 10, and 100)
* Displayable base-10 blocks, including a copy of one 100-flat with two squares cut out, or with 98 squares colored in
* Worksheets with additional problems (see activity 1.2b)
* Number cards, 1-9 and the tens 10-90, 2-4 sets per group
* Number cards, 0-9, 4 sets per group, plus six more 0's per group
* Hundreds board and counters for each group
* Number cubes, 4 per group

Homework

* Workbook Exercise 8
* Workbook Exercise 9
* Workbook Exercise 10
* Workbook Exercise 11
* Workbook Exercise 12
* Workbook Review 1

Notes

Mental Math strategies are reviewed here, and new ones are introduced. Some students may be using some of the new strategies already based on their own experience.

The following strategies will be reviewed or taught here.

➤ Subtract 1, 2, or 3 by counting back.
$51 - 2 = 49$; count back 50, 49.
$302 - 3 = 299$; count back 301, 300, 299

➤ Subtract a 1-digit number from a 2-digit or 3-digit number without renaming by subtracting ones from ones.
$155 - 4 = 151$

$155 - 4 = 150 + 5 - 4 = 151$

$150 \quad 5$

➤ Subtract 10, 20, or 30 by counting back.
$228 - 30 = 198$; count back 218, 208, 198 (or count back tens first and then add ones: 21, 20, 19 tens, 198.

➤ Subtract tens from each other without renaming.
$150 - 30 = 120$

➢ Subtract tens from a 2-digit or 3-digit number without renaming by subtracting from the tens.
    155 – 40 = 115

$155 - 40 = 110 + 5 = 115$
5   150

➢ Subtract a 1-digit number from a ten.
    430 – 7 = 423

$430 - 7 = 400 + 23 = 423$
400   30

➢ Subtract a 1-digit number from a 2-digit or 3-digit number when there are not enough ones by subtracting from a 10:
    176 – 8 = 168

$176 - 8 = 162 + 6 = 168$
6   170

➢ Subtract a 1-digit number from a 2-digit or 3-digit number by renaming a ten as ones and recalling the subtraction fact.
    176 – 8 = 168

$176 - 8 = 160 + 8 = 168$
160   16

➢ Subtract tens from a 3-digit number by subtracting the tens using the same strategies as subtracting ones from a 2-digit number
    433 – 70 = 430 – 70 + 3 = 360 + 3 = 363
    (43 – 7 = 36, so 430 – 70 = 360, add on the ones)

➢ Subtract hundreds from a 3-digit number by subtracting hundreds from hundreds.
    834 – 500 = 334

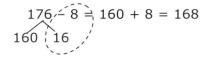
$834 - 500 = 300 + 34 = 334$
34   800

➢ Subtract a 2-digit numbers from a 2-digit number by subtracting first the tens and then the ones.
    75 – 38 = 75 – 30 – 8 = 45 – 8 = 37

➢ Subtract a number close to 100 by first subtracting 100 and then adding back the difference.
    456 – 98 = 456 – 100 + 2 = 356 + 2 = 358

Some students may be able to extend the strategies given in this section. Other students may be more comfortable with using the standard subtraction algorithm. Encourage students to use mental math where possible, but if they prefer, let them stick with the standard algorithm.

Activity 1.3a   **Subtract ones or tens**

1. Illustrate mental subtraction of ones from a 2-digit number
   when renaming occurs.
   - Use number discs. Display 5 tens and 4 ones. Tell
     students you want to subtract 8. Write the expression
     54 – 8 and discuss strategies to mentally find the value
     of 54 – 8.

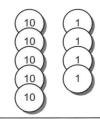

$$54 - 8 = \underline{\quad}$$

$$54 - 8 = \mathbf{4}\_$$

- Find the tens. Before determining the tens for the
  answer, look to the ones. Will subtracting 8 decrease
  the tens? Yes, so subtract 1 from the tens. Write 4 for
  the tens.
- Find the ones. Discuss two methods for finding the
  ones:
  1. Use the subtraction fact 14 – 8 = 6 to find the ones.
     You can illustrate this with the number discs by
     taking one of the tens, replacing with 10 ones, and
     removing 8 of them. 6 are left.
  2. Subtract from a ten and add the difference to the
     ones. Show this by replacing a ten with 2 ones, and
     then combining the 2 ones with the 4 ones already
     there. There will be 6 ones.
     Write 6 for the ones.

$$54 - 8 = 40 + 6 = 46$$
$$\diagup \diagdown$$
$$40 \quad 14$$

$$54 - 8 = 44 + 2 = 46$$
$$\diagup \diagdown$$
$$44 \quad 10$$

$$54 - 8 = 4\mathbf{6}$$

- Write the expression 21 – 2. Tell students that if they are
  subtracting a small number such as 1, 2, or 3, they can
  simply count back: 20, 19.

$$21 - 2 = 19$$

- Write the expression 55 – 4. Ask students to look at the
  ones. Point out that in this problem the tens will not be
  increased. So the tens digit stays the same, and we can
  just subtract the ones.

$$55 - 4 = 51$$

- Write other problems on the board involving subtraction of
  ones from a 2-digit number, particularly problems where
  there is renaming, and have the students find the answers
  mentally. Ask them what strategy they used.
- Display 4 tens and 4 ones. Write the expression 44 – 20.
  Point out that since we are subtracting tens, we can
  simply subtract from tens from tens to get the tens, and
  the ones in the answer stays the same. When subtracting
  smaller tens (10, 20, 30) we can also count back by tens

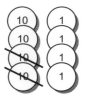

$$44 - 20 = 24$$

2. Have students do **task 1, text p. 16**.
   - You can use Mental Math 8 on the next page for additional practice or review, now or
     later.

Workbook Exercise 8

Mental Math 8

1.   90 – 8 = _____

2.   45 – 9 = _____

3.   21 – 6 = _____

4.   94 – 8 = _____

5.   82 – 4 = _____

6.   35 – 6 = _____

7.   64 – 8 = _____

8.   75 – 7 = _____

9.   53 – 9 = _____

10. 94 – 7 = _____

11. 33 – 4 = _____

12. 32 – 9 = _____

13. 42 – 6 = _____

14. 75 – 8 = _____

15. 71 – 2 = _____

16. 42 – 7 = _____

17. 73 – 8 = _____

18. 30 – 6 = _____

19. 86 – 8 = _____

20. 67 – 9 = _____

21. 62 – 7 = _____

22. 53 – 6 = _____

23. 55 – 8 = _____

24. 31 – 7 = _____

25. 83 – 4 = _____

26. 53 – 7 = _____

27. 34 – 5 = _____

28. 81 – 8 = _____

29. 46 – 9 = _____

30. 52 – 3 = _____

Activity 1.3b

1. Illustrate mental subtraction of ones, tens, or hundreds from a 3-digit number where there is no renaming. Use number discs.
   - Have students look at the **text p. 15** as they follow the discussion. Display 5 hundreds, 7 tens, and 8 ones.
   - Write the expression 578 – 4. Show that we can subtract the ones by removing ones. Ask for the digit in the ones place. We subtract 4 ones from 8 ones. Elicit the answer.
   - Write the expression 578 – 40. Show that we can subtract the tens by removing tens. Point to the tens in the written number. We subtract 4 tens from 7 tens. Elicit the answer.
   - Write the expression 578 – 400. Show that we can subtract the hundreds by removing hundreds. Ask for the digit in the hundreds place. We subtract 2 hundreds from 5 hundreds. Elicit the answer.

2. Illustrate mental subtraction of ones from a 3-digit number where there is renaming.
   - Start with the 3 hundreds, 5 tens, and 2 ones (or similar number). Write the expression 352 – 7.
     - Find the hundreds. Since we are not subtracting tens, the hundreds will stay the same. Write 3 for the hundreds.
     - Find 52 – 7 using the same strategies already discussed. Write down the answer, 45.
     - You can draw a number bond to illustrate the process.

3. Illustrate mental subtraction of tens from a 3-digit number where there is renaming.
   - Use number discs. Start with 3 hundreds, 5 tens, and 6 ones. Write the expression 356 – 80.
     - Since we are not subtracting ones, we can first think of just subtracting tens. 350 tens – 8 tens can be solved using the same strategies for 35 – 8. Ask students for the answer. 35 – 8 = 27, so 35 tens – 8 tens = 27 tens. Write 27 for the tens (2 hundreds and 7 tens).
     - Find the ones. They are simply the ones we started with. Write 6 for the ones.

Subtract ones, tens, or hundreds

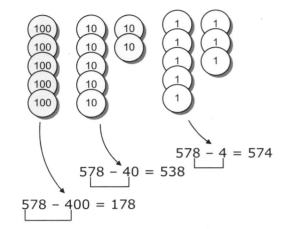

578 – 4 = 574

578 – 40 = 538

578 – 400 = 178

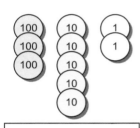

352 – 7 = **3__**

352 – 7 = **345**

352 – 7 = 300 + 52 – 7 = 345

```
     352 – 7
    /  X
  300  52
```

356 – 80 = **___**

356 – 80 = **27_**

356 – 80 = 27**6**

356 – 80 = 350 – 80 + 6 = 276

```
     356 – 80
    /  X
   6  350
```

- Write the expression 326 – 30. Explain that with smaller tens we can count down by tens: 31 tens, 30 tens, 29 tens, the answer is 296.

326 – 30 = 296

4. Have students do **task 2, text p. 16**.
   - Write other problems on the board involving subtraction of ones, tens, and hundreds from a 2-digit number. Call on students to find the answer mentally and explain verbally what strategy they used.
   - You can use the Mental Math 9 and 10 on the next two pages for additional practice or review, now or later.

Workbook Exercise 9

Activity 1.3c   **Practice**

Material for each group of students:
- Number cards 1-9 and 10, 20, 30, 40, 50, 60, 70, 80, and 90.
- Paper sheet with 2 columns, labeled as shown, with 900 in the *Totals* column, one for each student.

Subtract	Total
	900

Procedure:
- Cards are shuffled and placed face-down in the middle.
- Students take turns turning over a card and writing the number in the *Subtract* column. That student mentally subtracts the number (e.g. 40) from the previous total (900) and writes the new total (860) under the previous total.
- If the group agrees that the addition is correct, the old total is crossed out and the next student chooses a card, such as 2.
- All students can fill out one chart, using the numbers for each student's turn. If there is adequate time, or if this activity is done later when there is more time, students can fill out charts with only their own numbers.
- Play continues until each group or student reaches 900. Cards are reshuffled when needed.

Subtract	Total
	900
40	860
2	858
80	778

Mental Math 9

1. 190 – 8 = _____

2. 635 – 9 = _____

3. 121 – 6 = _____

4. 874 – 8 = _____

5. 824 – 6 = _____

6. 425 – 6 = _____

7. 754 – 8 = _____

8. 363 – 5 = _____

9. 751 – 9 = _____

10. 474 – 7 = _____

11. 245 – 6 = _____

12. 582 – 9 = _____

13. 550 – 4 = _____

14. 175 – 8 = _____

15. 666 – 8 = _____

16. 42 – 7 = _____

17. 882 – 8 = _____

18. 392 – 8 = _____

19. 826 – 8 = _____

20. 644 – 7 = _____

21. 714 – 9 = _____

22. 451 – 4 = _____

23. 953 – 6 = _____

24. 822 – 8 = _____

25. 666 – 9 = _____

26. 421 – 5 = _____

27. 331 – 7 = _____

28. 271 – 8 = _____

29. 421 – 9 = _____

30. 207 – 7 = _____

Mental Math 10

1. 278 – 10 = _____
2. 851 – 30 = _____
3. 611 – 10 = _____
4. 388 – 30 = _____
5. 292 – 30 = _____
6. 620 – 60 = _____
7. 760 – 30 = _____
8. 250 – 90 = _____
9. 720 – 60 = _____
10. 200 – 70 = _____
11. 620 – 70 = _____
12. 910 – 40 = _____
13. 500 – 80 = _____
14. 430 – 90 = _____
15. 220 – 30 = _____

16. 530 – 70 = _____
17. 230 – 80 = _____
18. 420 – 90 = _____
19. 710 – 70 = _____
20. 520 – 60 = _____
21. 610 – 30 = _____
22. 102 – 40 = _____
23. 547 – 70 = _____
24. 620 – 200 = _____
25. 830 – 100 = _____
26. 223 – 90 = _____
27. 732 – 500 = _____
28. 616 – 100 = _____
29. 122 – 80 = _____
30. 230 – 40 = _____

Activity 1.3d   **Subtract 2-digit numbers**

1. Illustrate mental subtraction of 2-digit numbers. Use number
    discs.
    - Write the expression 83 – 25 on the board and display a
      corresponding set of 83 number discs.
        o Have students first subtract the tens mentally and give
          the intermediate sum. Remove two 10-discs.
          83 – 20 = 63.
        o Have students then subtract the ones and give the final
          sum. Replace a 10-disc with ten 1-discs. 63 – 5 = 58.
    - Discuss **task 3, text p. 13**.

    $$83 - 25 = ?$$

    $$83 \xrightarrow{-20} 63 \xrightarrow{-5} 58$$

    $$83 - 25 = 58$$

2. Have student provide answers for **task 4, text p. 13**.
    - In the text and workbook, the problems don't involve renaming.
      Students can simply subtract tens from tens and ones from ones if
      they see that subtracting ones does not decrease the tens.
    - Do some additional examples, including some with renaming. This will be covered again
      in *Primary Mathematics 3B*.

Workbook Exercise 5

Activity 1.3e   **Game**

Material for each group of about 4 students:
- A hundreds number board.
- Four sets of number cards 0-9 and 6 extra cards with 0.
- Counters, one color per student.

Procedure:
- Cards are shuffled and placed face-down in the center.
- All students draw 4 cards. They then arrange the cards into two 2-digit numbers. If a 0
  is drawn, it can be used for the ones place or not used, in which case one of the
  numbers will be a 1-digit number. One number needs to be larger than the other. As
  soon as the student has formed the number and found the difference, he or she places a
  counter on the hundreds board to cover up an uncovered number corresponding to the
  answer. If it is already covered, the digits have to be rearranged to make different
  numbers and a different answer.
- Play continues until a student gets 3 counters in a row.

Activity 1.3f   **Subtract 98 or 99**

1. Illustrate subtraction of 98 and 99 from hundreds.
   You can use displayable base-10 blocks.
   - Write the expression 300 – 98 on the board.
     Display three 100-flats.
     ○ Ask students how they can use the idea of
       subtracting from 100 to mentally subtract
       these two numbers. They can subtract 98
       from one of the hundreds, leaving 2 ones.
     ○ Remove one of the hundreds and replace it
       with 2 ones. So the answer is one less
       hundred plus 2, or 202.
   - Point out that we can get the answer by
     subtracting 100 and then adding 2. If we just
     subtract 100, we have subtracted two too many,
     so we need to add it back in.
   - Repeat with 400 – 99. This time, we subtract 100
     and add 1.
   - You may also want to discuss subtraction of 97,
     96, and 95 from hundreds.
   - Discuss **task 5, text p. 17**.

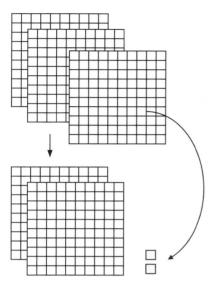

$$300 - 98 = 200 + 2 = 202$$

2. Have students supply answers to **task 6, text p. 17**.

3. Illustrate subtraction of 98 and 99 from a 3-digit
   number. You can use base-10 blocks.
   - Write 423 – 98 = ? on the board and display the
     corresponding number of hundreds, tens, and
     ones.
     ○ Lead students to see that if we subtract the
       98 from one of the hundreds, we will
       decrease the hundreds from 4 hundreds to 3
       hundreds, but leave 2 ones that are not
       removed. So we can find the answer by
       subtracting 100 and then adding 2.
   - Discuss **task 7, text p. 17**.

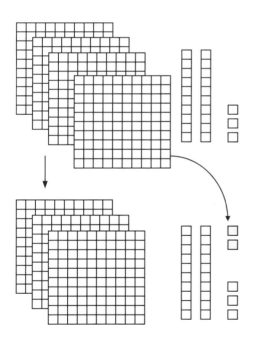

$$423 - 98 = 423 - 100 + 2 = 323 + 2 = 325$$

4. Have students supply answers to **tasks 8-9, text p. 17**.

5. You may want to extend the discussion to subtracting other numbers between 95 and 100 or subtracting a number close to a multiple of 100.
   - Ask students how they would solve 345 - 97 or 345 - 95.
   - Ask students how they would solve 648 – 398. They could subtract 400 and then add 2.

6. Give students additional problems for practice.
   - You can use the Mental Math 11 on the next two pages for additional practice or review, now or later.

Workbook Exercises 11-12

Activity 1.3g   **Practice**

Material for each group of about 4 students:
- One number cubes labeled with 0-5, one labeled with 5-9, and one labeled with 0, 2, 3, 5, 7, and 8 and one labeled with two each of 99, 98, and 97.

Procedure:
- Students take turns throwing the number cubes. They form a 3-digit number from the values on the cubes with single digits and subtract the number thrown on the cube with 99, 98, or 97. Other students check the answer.

Activity 1.3h   **Review and word problems**

1. Use **Practice 1B, text p. 18** and **Practice 1C, text p. 19** to review this unit.
   - Allow students to decide whether to use mental math or the addition or subtraction algorithms to solve these problems.
   - Note that mental techniques have not specifically been taught for problems 7 and 10 in Practice 1A or problems 1(c), 2(a), 2(b), 2(c), 3(b), 4(c), 5(a), 5(b), 8, or 10(a) in Practice 1B. You may, however, want to discuss how these could be solved mentally.
   - Discuss solutions for the word problems. Ask students to determine whether two parts are given and the whole must be found, or whether the whole and one part are given and a missing part must be found. Remind them that if they are missing the whole, they need to add the two parts to find the missing whole, and if they are missing a part, they need to subtract the other part from the whole to find the missing part. Students can draw number bonds to help them determine what equation to use. (See unit 2 of the *Teacher's Guide for Primary Mathematics 2A*).

Workbook Review 1

Mental Math 11

1. 200 – 98 = _____
2. 400 – 99 = _____
3. 500 – 99 = _____
4. 600 – 99 = _____
5. 100 – 97 = _____
6. 700 – 99 = _____
7. 360 – 99 = _____
8. 830 – 98 = _____
9. 810 – 98 = _____
10. 720 – 99 = _____
11. 432 – 99 = _____
12. 599 – 99 = _____
13. 742 – 98 = _____
14. 252 – 99 = _____
15. 433 – 99 = _____
16. 364 – 98 = _____
17. 786 – 99 = _____
18. 255 – 98 = _____
19. 259 – 99 = _____
20. 763 – 99 = _____
21. 464 – 98 = _____
22. 257 – 98 = _____
23. 203 – 98 = _____
24. 560 – 99 = _____
25. 702 – 99 = _____
26. 685 – 99 = _____
27. 886 – 198 = _____
28. 964 – 299 = _____
29. 513 – 398 = _____
30. 680 – 598 = _____

Unit 2 – Multiplication and Division

Objectives

- Count by fours, fives, and tens.
- Build multiplication tables for 4, 5 and 10.
- Memorize multiplication and division facts for 4, 5, and 10.
- Solve word problems involving multiplication by 4, 5, or 10.
- Solve word problems involving division by 4, 5, or 10.

Suggested number of sessions: 14

	Objectives	Textbook	Workbook	Activity
Part 1 : Multiplying and Dividing by 4				**6 sessions**
14	• Count by fours. • Write multiplication equations for fours.	pp. 20-21 p. 21 task 1	Ex. 13	2.1a
15	• Write two multiplication equations for a rectangular array. • Build multiplication table for 4.	p. 22, tasks 2-5	Ex. 14 -15	2.1b
16	• Solve word problems involving multiplication by 4. • Memorize multiplication facts for 4.		Ex. 16-17	2.1c
17	• Relate division facts to multiplication facts for 4.	pp. 23-24, tasks 6-8		2.1d
18	• Memorize division facts for 4. • Review other facts.		Ex. 18, #1-2	2.1e 2.1f
19	• Solve word problems.	p. 24, task 9 p. 25, Practice 2A	Ex. 18, #3	2.1g
Part 2 : Multiplying and Dividing by 5				**4 sessions**
20	• Count by fives. • Write multiplication equations for fives.	p. 26 pp. 27-28 tasks 1-5	Ex. 19	2.2a
21	• Solve word problems involving multiplication by 5. • Memorize multiplication facts for 5.		Ex. 20	2.2b
22	• Relate division facts to multiplication facts for 4. • Memorize division facts for 5.	p. 28, tasks 6-7	Ex. 21, #1-2	2.2c
23	• Solve word problems involving multiplication and division by 2, 3, 4, or 5.	p. 29, Practice 2B	Ex. 21, #3	2.2d
Part 3 : Multiplying and Dividing by 10				**2 sessions**
24	• Multiply by 10	p. 30 pp. 30-31, tasks 1-4	Ex. 22	2.3a
25	• Divide by 10 • Solve word problems. • Review multiplication and division by 10.	p. 31, tasks 5-6 p. 32, Practice 2C	Ex. 23	2.3b

Part 1: Multiplying and Dividing by 4 (pp. 20-25)   6 sessions

Objectives

- Count by fours.
- Build multiplication table for 4.
- Memorize multiplication facts for 4.
- Solve word problems involving multiplication by 4.
- Solve word problems involving division by 4.

Materials

- Connect-A-Cubes, multilink cubes, or 4-unit number bars (see activity 2.1a)
- Dot stickers
- Number board, four by ten (see activity 2.1a)
- Displayable counters
- Displayable color squares or base-10 set unit-cubes
- Number cubes labeled with 2, 2, 3, 3, 4 and 4, one per group
- Number cards 1-10 for each group
- Fact cards for multiplication and division by 2, 3, and 4 – multiplication or division fact on one side (e.g. 4 x 5) and answer on the reverse side one set per group
- Fact cards for division by 2, 3, and 4 with the fact on one side (e.g. 24 ÷ 4) but without the answer on the other side
- Division game sheet (see activity 2.1h)
- Counters for students

Homework

- Workbook Exercise 13
- Workbook Exercise 14
- Workbook Exercise 15
- Workbook Exercise 16
- Workbook Exercise 17
- Workbook Exercise 18

Notes

In *Primary Mathematics 2A*, students learned the multiplication and division facts for 2 and 3. They should be familiar with these facts. Incorporate review of these facts with the new facts that will be learned in this unit.

Both multiplication and division are associated with the part-whole concept.

Given the number of equal parts and the number in each part, we multiply to find the whole (total).

There are two division situations, sharing and grouping.

Sharing:
A total number (the whole) is shared into a given number of groups (parts). Divide the total by the number of parts to find the number in each part.

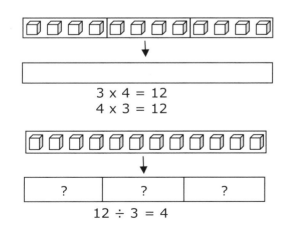

$$3 \times 4 = 12$$
$$4 \times 3 = 12$$

$$12 \div 3 = 4$$

Grouping:
A total number (the whole) is grouped into equal parts. Divide the total by the number that goes into each part to find the number of parts.

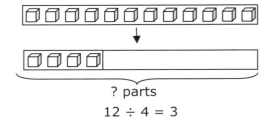

? parts

$12 \div 4 = 3$

Students learned to relate multiplication to division. The answer to $12 \div 4$ can be found by thinking of the number times 4 that equals 12.

$$3 \underset{\div\ 4}{\overset{\times\ 4}{\rightleftarrows}} 12$$

Students will be learning the facts for multiplication and division by 4 in this section. They will start by building the multiplication table of 4 based on the idea of "4 more than." If they know one fact for multiplication, they can find the next one as 4 more. They will use the multiplication facts for 4 to learn the division facts.

Review multiplication and division by 2, 3, and 4 regularly, either with multiplication and division cards, worksheets, or games. This guide includes some suggested games that can be played if time permits.

Square Graph Paper

Number Boards

1	2	3	4	5	6	7	8	9	10
11	12	13	14	15	16	17	18	19	20
21	22	23	24	25	26	27	28	29	30
31	32	33	34	35	36	37	38	39	40

1	2	3	4	5	6	7	8	9	10
11	12	13	14	15	16	17	18	19	20
21	22	23	24	25	26	27	28	29	30
31	32	33	34	35	36	37	38	39	40
41	42	43	44	45	46	47	48	49	50

Activity 2.1a   **Multiply by four**

1. Illustrate counting by fours.
   - Discuss **text p. 20**. Students should see that there are 4 stickers in each row. Have the students count by fours. Ask students questions such as, "How many stickers are there in 3 rows?"
   - Have students make 10 rows of 4 stickers in their journals and write the total next to them. They can use dot stickers or other stickers.
     - ○ Provide students with index cards. Ask them to cover up all their stickers with the index card and slide the card down so that only the first row is uncovered. Illustrate the process on the board or overhead projector (you can use transparent counters).
     - ○ Then ask them how many they would have if they uncovered the next row. They then slide the card down to check their answer.
     - ○ Point out that the next row is 4 more. They can add 4 to the number after the current row.
     - ○ Continue until all rows are uncovered.
   - Provide students with a number board through 40.
     - ○ Have students count and color the square for every fourth number. Discuss any patterns they see. For example, the colored number 24 is 20 more than the number above it (4).
     - ○ Have students practice counting by fours using the number board.

| 4 |
| 8 |
| 12 |
| 16 |
| 20 |
| 24 |
| 28 |
| 32 |
| 36 |
| 40 |

1	2	3	4	5	6	7	8	9	10
11	12	13	14	15	16	17	18	19	20
21	22	23	24	25	26	27	28	29	30
31	32	33	34	35	36	37	38	39	40

2. Write multiplication equations.
   - Provide students with connect-a-cubes or other linking cubes and have them link them into fours. (Or, copy the square graph paper onto cardstock, cut out 4-unit sections and distribute to the students.)
     - ○ Have students set out 6 groups of 4. Ask them how they would write an equation to show the total amount. They may write 4 + 4 + 4 + 4 + 4 + 4 = 24. Lead them to also write 4 x 6 = 24. There are 6 equal groups of 4.
     - ○ Repeat with other groups of 4.
     - ○ Write a multiplication fact on the board, such as 4 x 7. Have the students match a set of fours with the multiplication fact and count by fours to find the answer. Have them write the equation.
   - Discuss **text p. 21**, including task 1.

4 + 4 + 4 + 4 + 4 = 20

4 x 5 = 20

Workbook Exercise 13

Activity 2.1b   **Multiplication tables for four**

1. Illustrate the equivalency of 4 x ____ and ____ x 4
   - Provide students with connect-a-cubes linked in fours or 4-unit paper bars.
     - ○ Ask students to set out the number of bars that would give a total of 20. Demonstrate on the board or overhead projector. Have them write the equation 4 x 5 = 20.
     - ○ Ask them to push the bars together in an array. There are 5 rows of 4. Have them turn the array sideways. There are now 4 rows of 5. Write the equation 5 x 4 = 20. They now know two related multiplication facts.
   - Discuss **text p. 22, tasks 2-3.**
   - Write some other numbers in the number sequence for 4 (multiples of 4) on the board.
     - ○ Have students use their 4-unit bars to find the associated multiplication equations. For example, write 28 on the board. The associated equations are 4 x 7 = 28 and 7 x 4 = 28.

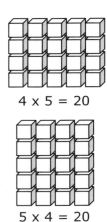

4 x 5 = 20

5 x 4 = 20

2. Build a multiplication table for four.
   - Display a 4 by 5 array.
     - ○ Ask students how many more cubes are needed to show 4 x 6. 4 x 6 is 4 more than 4 x 5. Add another 4-unit to the displayed bars.
     - ○ Point out that they can use the multiplication fact 4 x 5 = 20 to find 4 x 6 = 24 by adding 4 to the product of 4 and 5.

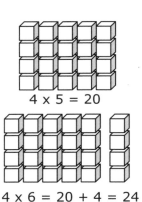

4 x 5 = 20

4 x 6 = 20 + 4 = 24

   -
     - ○ Remove a 4-unit to get back to 4 x 5 = 20. Ask students how many less is 4 x 4. Remove one of the 4-bars.
     - ○ Point out that if they know the multiplication fact for 4 x 5, they can find the one for 4 x 4 by subtracting 4.
   - Discuss **tasks 4-5, text pp. 22-23.** Have students copy task 4 into their journals. Encourage students to practice reciting the tables on their own.

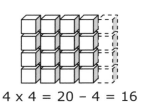

4 x 4 = 20 – 4 = 16

3. Practice multiplication facts for 4. This practice can be ongoing – spend a few minutes at the beginning of each class period providing fact practice.
   - Provide students with worksheets for practicing the multiplication by 2, 3, and 4, such as Mental Math 12 on the next page. In this worksheets, show students how to fill in the multiplication chart – the number that goes in each box is the product of the number at the top of the column and at the start of the row.
   - Do "sprints" (see Activity 1.2b) using multiplication problems.

Workbook Exercises 14-15

Mental Math 12

X	6	4	7	3	9	8	1	2	10	5
2										
3										
4										

X	2	8	3	6	1	9	5	4	7	10
4										
2										
3										

X	10	1	4	5	2	7	3	8	9	6
3										
4										
2										

Activity 2.1c   **Word problems and practice**

1. Discuss word problems involving multiplication.
    *   Use word problems similar to those in exercise 16 and 17, such as the following ones. They should determine what the problem wants them to find and what information is given. They should be able to tell you whether there are equal groups, how many equal groups, and how much is in each group. Have them write an equation for each problem. Allow them to act out the problem with drawings or with connect-a-cubes or other objects they can put into groups.

        ➤ Jeremy bought 4 books. Each book cost $6. How much did he pay for the books?

        ➤ A plastic bag can hold 4 apples. How many apples can 7 plastic bags hold?

        ➤ Marisol wants to wrap 6 presents. Each present needs 4 feet of ribbon. How many total feet of ribbon does she need to wrap all 6 presents?

        ➤ There are 8 rows of desks in a classroom. There are 4 desks in each row. There are 35 students. Are there enough desks for each student?

        ➤ There are 4 monkeys in a zoo. Each monkey eats 3 bananas in the morning and 4 bananas in the afternoon.
          a) How many bananas do they eat in the morning?
          b) How many bananas do they eat in the afternoon?
          c) How many bananas do they eat altogether?

    *   Include some problems involving multiplication by 2 or 3.

2. Continue to practice multiplication facts. Students can do the following in groups.
    *   Provide each group with multiplication cards.
        o The cards are placed in the middle, face up.
        o Students take turns choosing one, giving the answer, and turning over the card to check the answer.
        o The card is then removed from the center.
    *   Provide each group with 4 sets of number cards 1-10 and a number cube labeled with 2, 2, 3, 3, 4, and 4.
        o Cards are shuffled and dealt out.
        o Each student turns over a card, throws the number cube, and finds the product of the number on the cube and the number on the card.
        o The can be made into a game. The student with the highest product gets a point. If there is a tie both students get a point. The student with the most points after all cards have been turned over wins.
        o Or, students add their products after 5 or so rounds and the student with the highest sum wins.

Workbook Exercises 16-17

Activity 2.1d   **Divide by four**

1. Illustrate the relationship between division by 4 and multiplication by 4.
   - Display 24 objects, such as counters.
     - Tell students that we want to divide 24 objects into 4 equal groups. Draw 4 circles. Ask how many will go into each group.
     - Tell them that the total (point to it) divided by the number of equal groups (point to the circles) gives the number in each group.

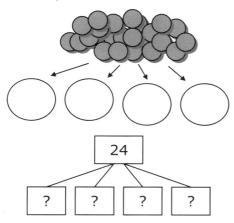

     - Draw a number bond with 4 parts with a question mark in each part.
     - Divide up the counters to show there are 6 in each group. Remind the students that the number in each group times the number of equal groups gives the total. If they can think of what number times 4 gives a total of 24 they will know how many are in each group. If 6 x 4 = 24, then 24 ÷ 4 = 6.
     - Write the equations
     - Draw an arrow diagram to show the relationship between multiplication and division.

$$24 \div 4 = 6$$
$$6 \times 4 = 24$$

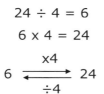

   - Put the counters back together in one group and tell the students that we now want to divide the counters into groups of 4.
     - Ask how many will go into each group. Lead students to see that they can still use the multiplication facts to think of the number times 4 which gives a total of 24.
     - You can illustrate this with a number bond showing an unknown number of parts.

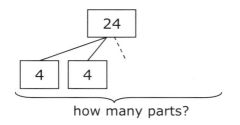

how many parts?

   - Arrange the counters in an array get the students to write two multiplication equations and 2 division equations.

   - Provide students with connect-a-cubes linked in fours or paper 4-unit rods.
     - Give them a number that is a multiple of 4 and let them use their bars to form an array and to write 2 multiplication equations and 2 division equations for the array.

$$4 \times 6 = 24 \qquad 24 \div 4 = 6$$
$$6 \times 4 = 24 \qquad 24 \div 6 = 4$$

• Write the equations shown here on the right on the board and have students copy them and fill in the blanks.	____ x 4 = 4 4 ÷ 4 = ____
	____ x 4 = 8 8 ÷ 4 = ____
	____ x 4 = 12 12 ÷ 4 = ____
	____ x 4 = 16 16 ÷ 4 = ____
	____ x 4 = 20 20 ÷ 4 = ____
	____ x 4 = 24 24 ÷ 4 = ____
	____ x 4 = 28 28 ÷ 4 = ____
	____ x 4 = 32 32 ÷ 4 = ____
	____ x 4 = 36 36 ÷ 4 = ____
	____ x 4 = 40 40 ÷ 4 = ____

2. Discuss text **tasks 6-8, text pp. 23-24**.
   • Have students supply the answers for **problems 1-5, Practice 2A, text p. 25.**

   Workbook Exercise 18, problems 1-2

Activity 2.1e   **Practice facts**

1. Provide students with an opportunity to memorize division facts for 4.
   • Students can work individually on practice problems, such as those in Mental Math 13 on the next page.
   • Students can work in small groups with division cards with answers on the back.
      ○ Cards are placed in the middle face up.
      ○ Students take turns choosing one, giving the answer, and turning over the card to check the answer.
      ○ The card is then removed from the center.

Activity 2.1f   **Game**

Material for each group:
   • Counters
   • A division game board with the numbers 1 through 10. Copy from p. 48 in this guide
   • A set of division cards with the division on one side (e.g. 24 ÷ 4) but without the answer on the back.

Procedure:
   • Each student selects a different color counter to serve as their marker.
   • Cards are shuffled and placed face down in the center.
   • Students take turns drawing a card and placing marker on an uncovered space on the board with the answer.
   • Cards are reshuffled as needed.
   • Play continues until a student gets 3 counters in a row.

Mental Math 13

1. $28 \div 4 =$ _____

2. $16 \div 4 =$ _____

3. $8 \div 4 =$ _____

4. $12 \div 3 =$ _____

5. $20 \div 4 =$ _____

6. $24 \div 4 =$ _____

7. $36 \div 4 =$ _____

8. $28 \div 4 =$ _____

9. $21 \div 3 =$ _____

10. $8 \div 4 =$ _____

11. $36 \div 4 =$ _____

12. $32 \div 4 =$ _____

13. $30 \div 3 =$ _____

14. $12 \div 4 =$ _____

15. $40 \div 4 =$ _____

16. $12 \div 4 =$ _____

17. $4 \div 4 =$ _____

18. $36 \div 4 =$ _____

19. $24 \div 4 =$ _____

20. $15 \div 3 =$ _____

21. $32 \div 4 =$ _____

22. $18 \div 3 =$ _____

23. $40 \div 4 =$ _____

24. $20 \div 4 =$ _____

25. $9 \div 3 =$ _____

26. $24 \div 3 =$ _____

27. $4 \div 4 =$ _____

28. $16 \div 4 =$ _____

29. $27 \div 3 =$ _____

30. $24 \div 4 =$ _____

Division Game Board

9	7	8	3	2	7	8
3	2	10	1	9	6	9
10	6	4	7	10	1	5
5	7	5	6	4	8	4
2	4	2	3	9	5	8
3	8	4	6	2	5	10
1	6	10	3	1	7	9

Activity 2.1g   **Word problems**

1. Discuss **task 9, text p. 24**.
   - Students can act out the problem or use diagrams. They need to see that both (a) and (b) give a total amount of money.
   - In (a), they are given the number of groups (4 days) and asked to find how much goes into each group (how much she saved each day).
   - In (b), they are given the number that goes in each group, and asked to find the number of groups. In both situations, they need to divide.

2. Discuss **problems 6-11, Practice 2A, text p. 25**.
   - Students should determine whether they need to divide or multiply to solve this problem. They can do this by acting out the problem with manipulatives or drawing pictures.
   - In problem 4 they can draw circles for each taxi and write 4 in each circle to show the number of passengers in each taxi. They need to find the total number of passengers. Since they have equal groups and the number in each group, they multiply to find the total.
   - In problem 5 they can draw a circle and write 16 in it to show how much coffee there is, and then 4 smaller circles to show the bags. They need to find the amount in each bag. Since they have a total amount of coffee and the number of bags, they need to divide to find the amount in each bag.
   - Emphasize that when they are asked to find a total, and have the number of equal parts and the number in each part, they multiply to find the total. When they have to find the number of equal groups or the number in each group, they divide the total.

3. Discuss a few challenging word problems such as the following. Guide the students in acting the problems out using objects or drawing pictures to solve the problem. Write equations for each step.

   ➢ A box of 4 toy cars cost $9. Josh bought 12 cars.
      a) How many boxes did he buy?
      b) How much did he pay?

   ➢ You have 24 toothpicks.
      a) How many equal sized squares can you form with the toothpicks? (6 with sides one toothpick long, or 3 with sides two toothpicks long)
      b) How many equal sized triangles of equal sides can you form with the toothpicks? (8 with sides 1 toothpick long, 4 with sides 2 toothpicks long)

   ➢ A cook makes 24 cookies and 20 brownies. Somebody ate 4 cookies and 5 brownies while they were cooling. The cook put 4 cookies and 3 brownies on each plate. How many plates did she use?

Workbook Exercise 18, problems 3-5

Part 2: Multiplying and Dividing by 5 (pp. 20-25)   4 sessions

Objectives

- Count by fives.
- Build multiplication table for 5.
- Memorize multiplication facts for 5.
- Solve word problems involving multiplication by 5.
- Solve word problems involving division by 5.

Materials

- Connect-A-Cubes or 5-unit number bars (see activity 2.1a)
- Dot stickers
- Number board, five by ten
- Displayable Counters
- Displayable color squares or base-10 set unit-cubes
- Number cubes labeled with 2, 3, 4, 4, 5, and 5, one for each group
- Number cards 1-10 for each group
- Fact cards for multiplication and division by 2, 3, 4, and 5
- Fact cards for division by 2, 3, 4, and 5 with the fact on one side (e.g. 35 ÷ 5) but without the answer on the other side
- Counters for students

Homework

- Workbook Exercise 19
- Workbook Exercise 20
- Workbook Exercise 21

Notes

Students will be learning the facts for multiplication and division by 5 in this section. They will start by building the multiplication table of 5 based on the idea of "5 more than." If they know one fact for multiplication, they can find the next one as 5 more. They will use the multiplication facts for 5 to learn the division facts.

Review multiplication and division by 2, 3, 4 and 5 regularly, either with multiplication and division cards, worksheets, or games.

Activity 2.2a   **Multiply by five**

1. Illustrate counting by fives. Use two or more of the following activities.

   - Discuss **text p. 26**. Point out that there are 5 cards in each group. Have the students count by fives. Ask students questions such as "How many cards are there in 6 groups?"

   - Provide students with dot stickers and index paper.
     - Have them make rows of 5 stickers in their journals and write the total next to them. They can use this to practice counting by fives.
     - They can use the index card to cover up the rows. They slide the cards down one row at a time, trying to remember the next number before uncovering it.

1	2	3	4	5	6	7	8	9	10
11	12	13	14	15	16	17	18	19	20
21	22	23	24	25	26	27	28	29	30
31	32	33	34	35	36	37	38	39	40
41	42	43	44	45	46	47	48	49	50

   - Provide students with a number board through 50.
     - Have students count and color the square for every fifth number. Discuss any patterns they see. For example, all the colored numbers end in 5 or 0.

   - Have students practice counting by fives.

   - Discuss **tasks 1-3, text pp. 27-28**. Have students write equations for task 3.
   - Provide students with connect-a-cubes linked in fives or the 5-unit bars.
     - Ask students set out the number of bars that would give a total of 30. Demonstrate on the board or overhead projector.
     - Ask them to push the bars together in an array. Have them write two multiplication equations for their array.
     - Ask students how many more cubes are needed to show 5 x 7. 5 x 7 is 5 more than 5 x 6. Have them add another 5-unit to the displayed bars. Point out that they can use the multiplication fact 5 x 6 = 30 to find 5 x 7 = 35 by adding 5 to the product of 5 and 6.
     - Ask students to write two multiplication equations for this array.

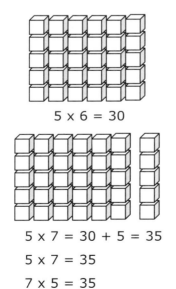

5 x 6 = 30

5 x 7 = 30 + 5 = 35

5 x 7 = 35

7 x 5 = 35

5 x 1 = _____	1 x 5 = _____
5 x 2 = _____	2 x 5 = _____
5 x 3 = _____	3 x 5 = _____
5 x 4 = _____	4 x 5 = _____
5 x 5 = _____	5 x 5 = _____
5 x 6 = _____	6 x 5 = _____
5 x 7 = _____	7 x 5 = _____
5 x 8 = _____	8 x 5 = _____
5 x 9 = _____	9 x 5 = _____
5 x 10 = _____	10 x 5 = _____

- Copy the equations at the right on the board. Have students copy them and supply the missing numbers.
- Have students recite the tables and encourage them to practice reciting the tables on their own.
- Discuss **text p. 28, tasks 4-5**.

Workbook Exercise 19

Activity 2.2b   **Word problems and practice**

1. Discuss word problems involving multiplication by 5, such as the following. Allow students to act out the problem with connect-a-cubes or other objects they can put into groups or use drawings.

   ➤ Melanie bought 5 dolls. Each doll cost $6. How much did she pay for the dolls?

   ➤ A box can hold 8 cupcakes. How many cupcakes can 5 such boxes hold?

   ➤ Cecily wants to sew 9 pillow cases. For each pillow case she needs 5 feet of material. How many feet of material does she need?

   ➤ There are 5 rows of desks in a classroom. There are 5 desks in each row. There are 30 students. Are there enough desks for each student?

   ➤ There are 7 elephants in a zoo. Each elephant eats 5 bundles of hay in the morning and 4 bundles in the afternoon.
      a) How bundles of had do they eat in the morning?
      b) How many bundles of hay do they eat in the afternoon?
      c) How many more bundles do they eat in the morning than in the afternoon?

2. Practice multiplication facts for 2, 3, 4, and 5. Use Mental Math 14 on the next page, or students can work in groups and do the following:
   - Provide each group with multiplication cards.
     o The cards are placed in the middle face up.
     o Students take turns choosing one, giving the answer, and turning over the card to check the answer.
     o The card is then removed from the center.
   - Provide each group with 4 sets of number cards 1-10 and a number cube labeled with 2, 3, 4, 4, 5, and 5.
     o Cards are shuffled and dealt out. Each student turns over a card, throws the die, and finds the product of the number on the die and the number on the card.
     o This can be played as a game. The student with the highest product gets a point. If there is a tie both get a point. The student with the most points after all cards have been turned over wins. Or, students add their products after 5 or so rounds and the student with the highest sum wins.

Workbook Exercise 20

Mental Math 14

X	6	4	3	5	10	2	1	8	9	7
3										
4										
5										

X	3	2	6	8	1	10	9	7	5	4
5										
3										
4										

X	7	1	4	2	3	5	8	6	9	10
2										
5										
3										

Activity 2.2c   **Divide by five**

1. Relate division facts to multiplication facts for 5.

    -   Remind students that to find a number divided by 5, such as 35 ÷ 5, they can think of the number times 5 that gives 35. Illustrate with objects, if necessary, as in activity 2.1d.
    -   Provide students with connect-a-cubes linked in fives or 5-unit rods. Give them a number that is a multiple of 5 and let them use their bars to form an array and to write 2 multiplication equations and 2 division equations for the array.
    -   Write a division problem on the board, such as 45 ÷ 5, and have them write the answer and the three other related equations. Include as review some division by 2, 3, or 4.
    -   Write the equations shown here on the board and have students copy into their journals, or create a handout for the students. Have them fill in the blanks.
    -   Discuss text **tasks 6-7, text p. 28**.

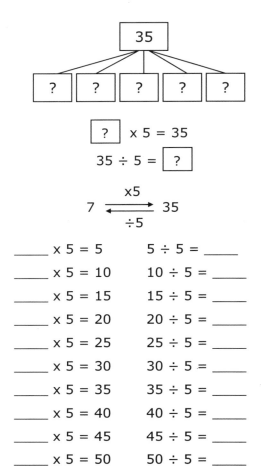

$$\text{____} \times 5 = 5 \qquad 5 \div 5 = \text{____}$$
$$\text{____} \times 5 = 10 \qquad 10 \div 5 = \text{____}$$
$$\text{____} \times 5 = 15 \qquad 15 \div 5 = \text{____}$$
$$\text{____} \times 5 = 20 \qquad 20 \div 5 = \text{____}$$
$$\text{____} \times 5 = 25 \qquad 25 \div 5 = \text{____}$$
$$\text{____} \times 5 = 30 \qquad 30 \div 5 = \text{____}$$
$$\text{____} \times 5 = 35 \qquad 35 \div 5 = \text{____}$$
$$\text{____} \times 5 = 40 \qquad 40 \div 5 = \text{____}$$
$$\text{____} \times 5 = 45 \qquad 45 \div 5 = \text{____}$$
$$\text{____} \times 5 = 50 \qquad 50 \div 5 = \text{____}$$

2. Have students supply the answers for **problems 1-5 Practice 2B, text p. 29.**

3. Provide opportunity for students to memorize the division facts.
    -   You can use Mental Math 15.
    -   Include division by 5 in "sprints".
    -   Students can play the game in activity 2.1f but including fact cards for division by 5.

Workbook Exercise 21, problems 1-2

Mental Math 15

1. $15 \div 3 = $ _____

2. $30 \div 5 = $ _____

3. $16 \div 4 = $ _____

4. $21 \div 3 = $ _____

5. $45 \div 5 = $ _____

6. $20 \div 5 = $ _____

7. $10 \div 5 = $ _____

8. $35 \div 5 = $ _____

9. $15 \div 5 = $ _____

10. $25 \div 5 = $ _____

11. $5 \div 5 = $ _____

12. $25 \div 5 = $ _____

13. $36 \div 4 = $ _____

14. $45 \div 5 = $ _____

15. $32 \div 4 = $ _____

16. $27 \div 3 = $ _____

17. $50 \div 5 = $ _____

18. $40 \div 5 = $ _____

19. $10 \div 5 = $ _____

20. $24 \div 4 = $ _____

21. $15 \div 5 = $ _____

22. $30 \div 5 = $ _____

23. $25 \div 5 = $ _____

24. $20 \div 5 = $ _____

25. $20 \div 4 = $ _____

26. $45 \div 5 = $ _____

27. $35 \div 5 = $ _____

28. $28 \div 4 = $ _____

29. $24 \div 4 = $ _____

30. $50 \div 5 = $ _____

Activity 2.2d   **Word problems**

1. Provide students with some problems involving multiplication and division by 5, such as those given below.
   - Students can act out the problem or use diagrams.
   - For a division problem, they need to see that they are given a total amount and either the number of equal groups and need to find the number that goes into each group, or they are given the number that goes into each group and need to find the number of groups.
   - For a multiplication problem, they need to see that they are given the number of equal groups and the number that goes into each group, and must find the total.
   - They should write the equations for each problem.

   ➢ A box of 25 cookies was shared among 5 children equally. How many cookies did each child get?

   ➢ A class of 30 students was divided into teams. There were 5 students on each team. How many teams were there?

   ➢ Each child has 10 fingers. How many fingers do 5 children have?

2. Discuss **problems 6-11, Practice 2B, text p. 29**.
   - Students should determine whether they need to divide or multiply to solve these problems. They can do this by acting out the problem with manipulatives or drawing pictures. They should write the equation for each problem.

2. Discuss a few more challenging problems, such as the following:

   ➢ A box of 40 cookies was shared among 5 boys.
     a) How many cookies did each boy get?
     b) How many cookies altogether did 4 of the boys get?
     c) If 5 of the cookies were dropped and could not be eaten, how many cookies would each of the 5 boys get?
     d) If one boy decided he did not want any of the 40 cookies, how many cookies would the rest of the boys get if they all got an equal number?

   ➢ On a test, 5 points were given for each correct answer and 3 points subtracted for each wrong answer. The test had 10 questions. Maria got 8 correct answers.
     a) How many points did she get for correct answers?
     b) How many points were subtracted for wrong answers?
     c) What was her final score?

Workbook Exercise 21, problems 3-6

Part 3: Multiplying and Dividing by 10 (pp. 30-32)   **2 sessions**

Objectives

- Count by tens.
- Build multiplication table for 10.
- Memorize multiplication facts for 10.
- Solve word problems involving multiplication by 10.
- Solve word problems involving division by 10.

Materials

- Rods from base-10 blocks or play money (dimes) for students
- Hundreds number board
- Displayable base-10 set rods
- Number cubes labeled with 2, 3, 4, 4, 5, and 10, one for each group
- Number cards 1-10 for each group
- Fact cards for multiplication and division by 2, 3, 4, 5, and 10
- Fact cards for division by 2, 3, 4, and 5 with the fact on one side (e.g. 40 ÷ 10) but without the answer on the other side
- Counters for students

Homework

- Workbook Exercise 22
- Workbook Exercise 23

Notes

Students will be learning the facts for multiplication and division by 10 in this section. They will use the multiplication facts for 10 to learn the division facts for 10.

Review multiplication and division by 2, 3, 4, 5, and 10 regularly, either with multiplication and division cards, worksheets, or games.

Hundreds Board

1	2	3	4	5	6	7	8	9	10
11	12	13	14	15	16	17	18	19	20
21	22	23	24	25	26	27	28	29	30
31	32	33	34	35	36	37	38	39	40
41	42	43	44	45	46	47	48	49	50
51	52	53	54	55	56	57	58	59	60
61	62	63	64	65	66	67	68	69	70
71	72	73	74	75	76	77	78	79	80
81	81	83	84	85	86	87	88	89	90
91	92	93	94	95	96	97	98	99	100

Activity 2.3a   **Multiply by 10**

1. Illustrate counting by 10
   • Discuss **text p. 30**. Point out that there are 10 eggs in each carton. Have the students count by tens. Students have counted by tens before when learning about place value, so this should be a review. Ask students questions such as, "How many eggs are there in 6 cartons?"
   • Provide students with a hundreds number board. Have students count and color in the square for every tenth number. Discuss any patterns they see. All the colored numbers end in 0.

1	2	3	4	5	6	7	8	9	10
11	12	13	14	15	16	17	18	19	20
21	22	23	24	25	26	27	28	29	30
31	32	33	34	35	36	37	38	39	40
41	42	43	44	45	46	47	48	49	50
51	52	53	54	55	56	57	58	59	60
61	62	63	64	65	66	67	68	69	70
71	72	73	74	75	76	77	78	79	80
81	82	83	84	85	86	87	88	89	90
91	92	93	94	95	96	97	98	99	100

2. Write equations for multiplying by ten.

   • Provide students with base-10 rods or dimes.
     ○ Write a multiplication fact on the board, such as 10 x 7. Have the students match a set of rods or dimes with the multiplication fact and count by tens to find the answer. Then ask them to write the related equation (7 x 10 = 70)
     ○ Repeat with other multiplication facts.

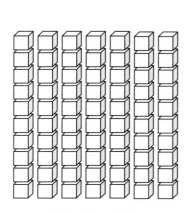

10 x 7 = 70
7 x 10 = 70

   • Copy the table at the right on the board. Have students copy the table into their journals and supply the missing numbers. Ask them if they see any patterns. A "0" is being added to the number being multiplied by 10. Multiplying a number by 10 is the same as putting the number in the next highest place value.

10 x 1 = _____	1 x 10 = _____
10 x 2 = _____	2 x 10 = _____
10 x 3 = _____	3 x 10 = _____
10 x 4 = _____	4 x 10 = _____
10 x 5 = _____	5 x 10 = _____
10 x 6 = _____	6 x 10 = _____
10 x 7 = _____	7 x 10 = _____
10 x 8 = _____	8 x 10 = _____
10 x 9 = _____	9 x 10 = _____
10 x 10 = _____	10 x 10 = _____

3. Discuss **tasks 1-4, text pp. 30-31**. Have students write equations for task 2

4. Adapt activities in parts 1 and 2 to practice the multiplication facts learned so far.

Workbook Exercise 22

Activity 2.3b   **Divide by 10**

1. Relate division facts to multiplication facts for 10.
   - Remind students that to find a number divided by 10, such as 70 ÷ 10, they can think of the number times 10 that gives 70. Illustrate with objects, if necessary, as in activity 2.1g
   - Write a division problem on the board, such as 80 ÷ 10, and have them write the answer and the three other related equations.
   - Write the equations shown here on the board and have students copy into their journals, or create a handout for the students. Have them fill in the blanks. Ask students if they see any patterns. To divide a ten by ten, they can remove a 0 from the ten.
   - Discuss text **tasks 5-6. text p. 31**.

80 ÷ 10 = 8
80 ÷ 8 = 10
10 x 8 = 80
8 x 10 = 80

_____ x 10 = 10	10 ÷ 10 = _____
_____ x 10 = 20	20 ÷ 10 = _____
_____ x 10 = 30	30 ÷ 10 = _____
_____ x 10 = 40	40 ÷ 10 = _____
_____ x 10 = 50	50 ÷ 10 = _____
_____ x 10 = 60	60 ÷ 10 = _____
_____ x 10 = 70	70 ÷ 10 = _____
_____ x 10 = 80	80 ÷ 10 = _____
_____ x 10 = 90	90 ÷ 10 = _____
_____ x 10 = 100	100 ÷ 10 = _____

2. Use **Practice 2C, text p. 32,** to review multiplication and division by 10. Call on students to supply the answers and explain their work for the word problems.

Workbook Exercise 23

Review

Objectives

• Review all topics.

Suggested number of sessions: 2

	Objectives	Textbook	Workbook	Activity
26	▪ Review.	p. 33, Practice 2D p. 34, Practice 2E	Review 2	R.1
27		p. 35, Review A		

Activity R.1   **Review**

1. Use **Practice 2D, text p. 33** and **Practice 2E, text p. 34** to review multiplication and division by 10. Call on students to supply the answers and explain their work for the word problems.

2. Use **Review A, text p. 35** to review addition, subtraction, multiplication, and division. Call on students to supply the answers and explain their work for the word problems.

3. Provide additional review as necessary. In particular, provide review for the mental math strategies learned in unit 1. You can use the Mental Math worksheets on the following pages.

Workbook Review 2

Mental Math 16

1. $31 - 4 =$ _____

2. $130 + 90 =$ _____

3. $78 - 20 =$ _____

4. $24 + 71 =$ _____

5. $670 + 30 =$ _____

6. $200 - 77 =$ _____

7. $350 + 80 =$ _____

8. $489 + 300 =$ _____

9. $283 + 99 =$ _____

10. $305 - 8 =$ _____

11. $361 + 8 =$ _____

12. $418 + 98 =$ _____

13. $631 - 98 =$ _____

14. $630 - 70 =$ _____

15. $872 - 50 =$ _____

16. $53 + 24 =$ _____

17. $643 - 60 =$ _____

18. $77 + 50 =$ _____

19. $390 - 98 =$ _____

20. $200 + 730 =$ _____

21. $57 + 8 =$ _____

22. $95 - 42 =$ _____

23. $245 + 60 =$ _____

24. $884 - 100 =$ _____

25. $100 - 81 =$ _____

26. $588 - 99 =$ _____

27. $203 + 8 =$ _____

28. $428 - 3 =$ _____

29. $100 - 25 =$ _____

30. $97 + 655 =$ _____

Mental Math 17

1. $4 \times 8 =$ _____

2. $9 \times 4 =$ _____

3. $8 \times 5 =$ _____

4. $32 \div 4 =$ _____

5. $20 \div 4 =$ _____

6. $4 \times 5 =$ _____

7. $4 \times 2 =$ _____

8. $4 \times 4 =$ _____

9. $25 \div 5 =$ _____

10. $6 \times 5 =$ _____

11. $8 \times 4 =$ _____

12. $45 \div 5 =$ _____

13. $35 \div 5 =$ _____

14. $10 \times 5 =$ _____

15. $3 \times 5 =$ _____

16. $28 \div 4 =$ _____

17. $7 \times 4 =$ _____

18. $5 \times 7 =$ _____

19. $20 \div 5 =$ _____

20. $10 \times 4 =$ _____

21. $24 \div 4 =$ _____

22. $5 \times 9 =$ _____

23. $30 \div 5 =$ _____

24. $5 \times 5 =$ _____

25. $36 \div 4 =$ _____

26. $16 \div 4 =$ _____

27. $40 \div 5 =$ _____

28. $4 \times 6 =$ _____

29. $10 \div 5 =$ _____

30. $15 \div 5 =$ _____

Mental Math 18

1. $6 \times 10 =$ _____

2. $10 \times 10 =$ _____

3. $4 \times 7 =$ _____

4. $12 \div 3 =$ _____

5. $4 \times 3 =$ _____

6. $5 \times 7 =$ _____

7. $18 \div 3 =$ _____

8. $5 \times 4 =$ _____

9. $9 \div 3 =$ _____

10. $10 \times 9 =$ _____

11. $2 \times 2 =$ _____

12. $27 \div 3 =$ _____

13. $70 \div 10 =$ _____

14. $5 \times 5 =$ _____

15. $5 \times 9 =$ _____

16. $32 \div 4 =$ _____

17. $8 \times 10 =$ _____

18. $15 \div 3 =$ _____

19. $3 \times 6 =$ _____

20. $3 \times 3 =$ _____

21. $24 \div 4 =$ _____

22. $21 \div 3 =$ _____

23. $27 \div 3 =$ _____

24. $24 \div 3 =$ _____

25. $100 \div 10 =$ _____

26. $2 \times 5 =$ _____

27. $8 \div 2 =$ _____

28. $80 \div 10 =$ _____

29. $12 \div 4 =$ _____

30. $2 \times 3 =$ _____

Unit 3 – Money

Objectives

- Count sets of bills and coins.
- Recognize, read, and write decimal notation for money.
- Make change mentally for $1 or $10.
- Add and subtract money within $10.
- Solve word problems involving addition and subtraction of money.

Suggested Number of sessions: 18

	Objectives	Textbook	Workbook	Activity
Part 1 : Dollars and Cents				**6 sessions**
28	• Count money in a set of bills and coins. • Recognize, read, and write the decimal notation for money.	pp. 36-37	Ex. 24	3.1a
29	• Write amounts of money in words and figures.	pp. 37-38, tasks 1-3	Ex. 25 Ex. 26	3.1b
30	• Convert money from one denomination to another or between dollars and cents to cents.	pp. 38-39, tasks 4-9	Ex. 27	3.1c 3.1d
31	• Make change for $1.	p. 40, tasks 10-12	Ex. 28	3.1e 3.1f
32	• Make change for $10.	p. 40, tasks 13-14	Ex. 29	3.1g
33	• Solve word problems.	p. 41, Practice 3A	Ex. 30	3.1h
Part 2 : Adding Money				**5 sessions**
34	• Add money by adding dollars and cents separately.	p. 42 p. 43, tasks 1-3	Ex. 31	3.2a
35	• Add money within $10 by first adding dollars, then cents.	p. 43, tasks 4-5	Ex. 32	3.2b 3.2c
36	• Add money within $10 using the formal algorithm for addition.	p. 44, tasks 6-7	Ex. 33	3.2d
37	• Add money using mental strategies.	p. 44, tasks 7-8	Ex. 34	3.2e
38	• Solve word problems involving the addition of money.	p. 45, tasks 9-10		3.2f 3.2g
Part 3 : Subtracting Money				**6 sessions**
39	• Subtract money by subtracting dollars and cents separately.	p. 46 p. 47, tasks 1-3	Ex. 35	3.3a
40	• Subtract money within $10 by first subtracting dollars, then cents.	p. 47, tasks 4-5	Ex. 36	3.3b 3.3c
41	• Subtract money within $10 using the subtraction algorithm.	p. 48, task 6	Ex. 37	3.3d
42	• Subtract money using mental strategies	p. 48, tasks 7-8	Ex. 38	3.3e
43	• Solve word problems.	p. 49, tasks 9-10	Ex. 29	3.3f 3.3g
44	• Practice.	p. 50, Practice 3B p. 51, Practice 3C		3.3h

Part 1: Dollars and Cents (pp. 36-41)   **6 sessions**

Objectives

- Count money in a set of bills and coins.
- Read and write decimal notation for money.
- Convert dollars and cents to cents.
- Convert cents to dollars and cents.
- Write amounts of money in words and figures.
- Make change for bills of $1, $5, and $10.

Materials

- Play money.
- Displayable bills and coins (such as overhead bills and coins)
- Store cards – index cards with pictures of items with a price of less than $1 marked in cents (use multiples of 5 for the cents)
- Store cards – index cards with pictures of items with a price of less than $10 (use multiples of 5 for the cents)
- Coupon or advertisements from newspapers with amounts of money less than $100

Homework

- Workbook Exercise 24
- Workbook Exercise 25
- Workbook Exercise 26
- Workbook Exercise 27
- Workbook Exercise 28
- Workbook Exercise 29
- Workbook Exercise 30

Notes

Students learned to count money in a set of coins (up to $1) or a set of bills (up to $10) in *Primary Mathematics 1B*. Here they will learn to count money in sets of bills and coins up to $100, to convert from dollars and cents to cents and vice-versa, and to make change for $1, $5, and $10. Students will also write amounts of money up to $100 in words.

The concept of decimals has not yet been taught. The decimal point should be presented as a dot separating dollars from cents. Decimals will be taught more completely *in Primary Mathematics 4B*.

In making change for $1, students can count up with coins, generally starting with the smallest denomination. They can practice making change in different ways. In subtracting from $1, students can use mental math skills for making 100 learned in the first unit of *Primary Mathematics 2B*.

In making change for $10, they will make change up to the next dollar, and then count up to $10. In subtracting from $10, students can use mental math skills to make 100¢ and $9 ($10 = $9 + 100¢).

3rd edition: The term ***bills*** will be used for ***notes*** in this guide. Substitute activities involving whatever coin and bill denominations your country uses for these activities.

Activity 3.1a   **Dollars and cents**

1. Review counting and writing an amount of money in coins. Use coins that can be displayed, such as those for overhead projectors.
   - US edition: Display one quarter and ask students for the amount of money. Repeat with 2, 3, and 4 quarters. Students should be able to easily recall that 2 quarters are 50 cents, 3 quarters are 75 cents, and 4 quarters are $1.
   - 3rd edition: If your country used a coin denomination of 20 cents, then have your students find the amount of money in 2, 3, 4, and 5 twenty-cent coins.
   - Display a set of nickels [5-cent coins] (less than 20) and have students count the amount of money by counting by fives.
   - Display a set of coins less than $1 and discuss strategies for counting the money.
     - We can count the coins by first counting by the amount in the largest denomination, and then going to each smaller denomination in order, i.e. by 25's for the quarters [or 20-dent coins], then by 10's for dimes [10-cent coins], then by 5's for nickels [5-cent coins], then by 1's for pennies [1-cent coins].
     - We can also combine coins to make a convenient amount (i.e. a quarter and a nickel for 30 cents and then count by 10's for dimes). Write the total amount as the number of cents (e.g. 65¢).

2. Review counting and writing an amount of money in bills. Use bills that can be displayed.
   - Display a set of bills less than $100.
     - Discuss strategies for counting the money.
     - Write the total amount (e.g. $41).

3. Discuss counting and writing an amount of money in both bills and coins.
   - Display an amount of money consisting of bills and coins less than $100 where the total amount in coins is less than a dollar.
     - Write the total amount in figures, for example $42.31. Tell students that when we have both dollars and cents, we write a dollar sign, the total number of dollars, a dot, and then the total number of cents. We do not write a cent sign after the cents. We read the amount as dollars and cents (e.g. "forty-two dollars and thirty-one cents").
   - Display a set of coins less than $1.
     - Have students find the total amount.
     - Write the amount in dollars (e.g. $0.45). Tell students this shows that there are zero dollars and 45 cents.
   - Display a set of coins and bills where there are less than 10 cents in coins.
     - Show students that if there are less than 10 cents, we write a 0 for the tens after the dot separating dollars and cents. For example we write $1.04 for a dollar and 4 cents, not $1.4. Tell them there have to be two digits for the number of cents if there are any cents. If there are no tens, they must put in a 0 as a place-holder for tens.
   - Display a set of bills and coins where the coins add up to $1 exactly.
     - Ask them to write the amount.
     - Tell them they can write the total amount as the dollar amount only, such as $23, or include the dot and two zeros as place-holders for the cents, $23.00.

4. Discuss **text pp. 36-37 and task 1, text p. 37**.
   - Have students write the amounts in task 1 as dollars, e.g. $33.30.

Workbook Exercise 24

Activity 3.1b   **Write money amounts in words**

1. Review spelling of number words.

2. Write money amounts in words.
    * Tell students that sometimes we need to be able to write the amount of money in words, such as when writing checks or on legal documents.
    * Discuss **tasks 2-3, text p. 38**. Have students say the amounts. Then write out the amounts using number words on the board, e.g. "seventeen dollars and ninety-five cents". Have students copy into their journals.
    * Have students write the amounts for **task 1, text p. 37** in words.
    * Write some amounts in words and have students copy and then write the amount in figures.
    * Write some amounts in figures and have students copy and then write the amounts in words. Be sure to include some amounts where the number of cents is less than 10 cents.

3. Divide students into small groups and have them do one or more of the following activities.
    * Provide each group with a set of money and have them count and write down the amount in both figures and words.
    * Provide each group with some store cards and some money. Students select a card, read the amount of money on the card, write it in words, and then count out the correct amount of money they would need to pay for it.
    * Divide students into groups.
    * Provide each group with a page from a newspaper and or a set of coupons and have students list all the money amounts they can find and then write the amount out in words.
    * Provide each group with money. Students take turns setting out an amount of money for the rest of the group to count and write in words.

Workbook Exercises 25-26

Activity 3.1c   **Change denomination**

1. Discuss changing money from one denomination to another.
    * Discuss **task 4, text p. 38** and **task 6(a), text p. 39.** You can display these amounts, and have students count the money.
    * U.S.: Have students give you the names for one-cent coins, five-cent coins, and ten-cent coins)
    * Discuss other examples for changing from one denomination of coins to another for amounts less than $1. For example:
        o How many nickels [5-cent coins] can be changed for a quarter [or a 20-cent coin]?
        o How many nickels, dimes, or quarters [5-cent coins, 10-ceint coins, 20-cent coins] can be changed for a half-dollar?
        o How many nickels [5-cent coins] can be changed for a quarter [or 20-cent coin]?
    * Discuss **tasks 6(b), text p. 39**.
    * Ask students for other ways to change from one denomination of bills to another. For example:
        o How many twenty dollar bills can be changed for a hundred dollar bill?
        o How many ten dollar bills can be changed for a fifty dollar bill?

- Discuss **task 7, text p. 39**.
  - Ask students for a different way that Melissa could have had $23. Display the $23 using the same denominations and trade in some bills for other bills. You can make a list like the one here. There are 8 ways that she could have $23 with just bills.
- Play a guessing game with the students.
  - Pick out a set of coins less than $1, but don't show it to them. Tell them the total amount and the number of coins. See if students can tell you what coins you have. They can use coins to help them come up with the answer. For example, tell students you have 7 coins and a total of 63¢. They tell you that you have 2 quarters, 2 nickels, and 3 pennies.
  - Do the same with bills, or bills and coins. For example, tell students you have 2 bills and 2 coins and a total of $6.30. They tell you that you have a $5 bill, a $1 bill, a quarter, and a nickel. Keep the number of bills and coins small.

$20	$10	$5	$1
1			3
	2		3
	1	2	3
	1	1	8
	1		13
		2	13
		1	18
			23

2. Discuss writing money from dollars and cents or as just cents.
   - Display a dollar bill. Write $1. Ask how we would write it in both dollars and cents. There are no cents, so we can write it as $1.00. Ask how we would write it just as cents. $1.00 = 100¢
   - Display a set of coins greater than $1 but less than $2. Have students count the money. Write the amount as cents (e.g. 145¢). Then trade in a 100¢ of coins for $1. Write the amount as dollars and cents (e.g. 145¢ = $1.45). Repeat with some other sets of coins, and then with some sets of bills and coins less than $10.
   - Discuss **tasks 5** and **8-9, text pp. 38-39**. For task 5 have students also write the amount as the total number of cents.

Workbook Exercise 27

Activity 3.1d   **Enrichment**

Material for each group:
- Bills and coins.
- Blank chart with columns for coin or bill denominations. (The chart shown at the right is for U.S. coin denominations.)

Procedure:
- Have each group see how many coin combinations there are that make a 25¢. They should record their combinations. When they are finished, see which group came up with the most combinations. (U.S. coins: There are 13 ways to make 25¢ with quarters, dimes, nickels, or pennies.)
- Have each group see how many coin combinations there are that make $1. (US: There are 292 different possible coin combinations)
- Have the groups find different combinations of bills that make a given amount, such as $10.

quarter	dime	nickel	penny
1			
	2	1	
	2		5
	1	3	
	1	2	5
	1	1	10
	1		15
		5	
		4	5
		3	10
		2	15
		1	20
			25

Activity 3.1e   **Make change for $1**

1. Discuss making change for $1. Use coins that you can display.
   - Tell students you want to buy something that costs 13¢ and pay for it with $1. Ask how much change you would receive. Discuss different ways to make change, illustrating with the coins.
   - Students can count up to 15¢ with 2 pennies, then to 25¢ with a dime, then to 50¢, 75¢, and $1 with quarters.
   - Ask how you would make change if you had no dimes or no quarters.
   - Repeat with a few other examples.

2. Illustrate subtraction from $1 as a computation problem, rather than counting out change.
   - Write a problem on the board, such as $1 - 35¢. Remind students that $1 = 100¢. Write 100 – 35.
   - Discuss ways to make 100, which they learned in unit 1. They can count up by tens and then ones, or by ones and then tens, or find the digit that makes 9 with the first digit and 10 with the second digit.

3. Discuss **tasks 10 -12, text p. 40**.

   Workbook Exercise 27

Activity 3.1f   **Store**

1. Use a store theme to get students to practice making change for $1.
   - Set up shop with the store cards or tagged items priced at less than $1.
   - Assign a fourth to a third of the students to be cashiers. Provide them with coins to make change.
   - Give other students five $1 bills and a chart to record their purchases.

item	cost	paid	change
pencil	45¢	$1	55¢
pen	50¢	50¢	0
book	83¢	$1	17¢

   - Students purchase one item at a time until they have spent their money. The cashier must make correct change.
   - Students record the items bought, the money given the cashier, and the change.
   - Have students take turns being cashiers.
   - This can also be played in groups if time is limited. In this case, there is no cashier but a central pool of change. Each group gets some store cards. Students select an item, pay into the central pool, and collect change. They record their purchases.

Activity 3.1g   **Make change for $5 or $10**

1. Illustrate making change for $5 or $10. Use displayable coins.
   - Tell students you want to buy something that costs some amount less than $5, such as $3.45, and pay for it with $5.
   - Discuss ways to make change, illustrating with overhead coins. Count out coins up to the next $1, and then $1 bills up to $5.
   - Repeat with making change for a purchase under $10 using a $10 bill.

2. Discuss mental math strategies for finding the difference when subtracting from $10.
   - Write a problem on the board, such as $10 - $5.35. Show that $10 is the same as $9 and 100¢. Ask students for suggestion on how they can use this information to mentally find the difference.
   - They can find the difference between $9 and $5 for the dollar portion of the answer, and make 100 with the 35 for the cent portion of the answer.

$10 - $5.35
$9   100¢

$9 - $5 = $4
                $4.65
100¢ - 35¢ = 65¢

3. Discuss **tasks 13 -14, text p. 40**.
   - Do some additional problems involving subtraction from $10 or from $5.

4. Do a variation of activity 3.4f, using store cards or tagged items priced at less than $10. You can have students record their purchases and change.

item	cost	paid	change
doll	$3.45	$10	$6.55
book	$2.40	$5	$2.60
bear	$6.25	$10	$3.75
ruler	55¢	$1	45¢

Workbook Exercise 29

Activity 3.1h   **Practice**

1. Use **Practice 3A, text p. 41** to practice and review material learned so far in this unit.

2. Provide additional practice.
   - Students can play the guessing game (see activity 3.1c) with each other. One student picks out some coins or bills and coins which the other students do not see. He or she then tells the rest of the group the total amount and the total number of bills and coins. Students try to guess exactly how much of each kind of bill or coin s/he has.
   - You can have the students play store (see activity 3.1f).

| **Part 2: Adding Money (pp. 42-45)** | **5 sessions** |

Objectives

- Add money within $10.
- Solve word problems involving the addition of money.

Materials

- Play money
- Overhead bills and coins
- Store cards – index cards with pictures of items with a price of less than $10 (use multiples of 5 for the cents)

Homework

- Workbook Exercise 31
- Workbook Exercise 32
- Workbook Exercise 33
- Workbook Exercise 34

Notes

Students will learn the following strategies for adding money within $10.

Add the dollars and then add the cents. For example, add $4.15 and $3.50 by first adding $4 and $3 to get $7, then adding 15¢ and 50¢ to get 65¢; the sum is $7.65. The problems at this level will only use multiples of 5 for the cents to facilitate mental addition. They will be able to add the cents mentally by adding tens and then adding another five to the next ten if both numbers have fives (e.g. 35¢ + 45¢ = 35¢ + 40¢ + 5¢ = 75¢ + 5¢ = 80¢). If the cents add up to a dollar, they increase the dollar amount by 1.

Use the formal algorithm for addition. Write the problem vertically, aligning the dots (decimals) and add using the same methods as with whole numbers. Students can use the formal algorithm when they cannot solve the problem mentally.

Add money by first making a whole number of dollars. This method can be used when the cents add to more than a dollar, particularly when it is easy to see what needs to be added to one set of money to make a whole dollar, and what remains when this is amount is subtracted from the other set of money.

$$\$6.25 + \$1.85$$

$$\$6.25 + \$1.85 = \$7.25 + \$0.85 = \$8 + \$0.10 = \$8.10$$
$$\underset{\$0.75 \quad \$0.10}{\diagup \quad \diagdown}$$

Add a whole number of dollars, and subtract the difference. This method can be used when the cents in the amount being added are close to 100.

$$\$6.25 + \$2.95$$

$$\$6.25 \xrightarrow{\ +\$3\ } \$9.25 \xrightarrow{\ -5¢\ } \$9.20$$

Activity 3.2a   **Add cents or dollars**

1. Illustrate adding dollars to dollars and cents.
   - Display two sets of money, one with bills and coins and one with just bills. The total should be less than $10.
   - Have the students count the money in each set, and then find the total amount by adding the dollars together.
   - Have them write the addition equation.

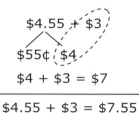

$4 + $3 = $7

$$\boxed{\$4.55 + \$3 = \$7.55}$$

2. Illustrate adding cents to dollars and cents.
   - Display two sets of money, one with bills and coins and one with just coins. The total coins should be less than $1.
   - Have the students count the money in each set, and then find the total amount by adding the cents together.
   - Have them write the addition equation.

$4.25 ⤻ 35¢

$4   25¢

35¢ + 25¢ = 60¢

$$\boxed{\$4.25 + 35¢ = \$4.60}$$

3. Illustrate adding money by adding the dollars and cents separately.
   - Display two sets of money containing both bills and coins. The total amount should be less than $10 and the total coins less than $1.
   - Have the students count the money in each set, and then add the dollars together first and the cents together.
   - Have them write the addition equation.

$4.25   + $3.35

$4   25¢ $3   35¢

$4 + $3 = $7
25¢ + 35¢ = 60¢

$$\boxed{\$4.25 + \$3.35 = \$7.60}$$

4. Discuss **text p. 42 and tasks 1-3, text p. 43**.
   - In task 3, students should notice that the cents add to $1 so the total dollar amount in increased by 1. Illustrate some of these with money, if necessary.

Workbook Exercise 31

Activity 3.2b   **Add dollars and cents**

1. Illustrate adding money by adding the dollars first and then the cents.
   - Display two sets of money, such as $4.25 and $3.35.
     - Tell students they can add these by adding $3 to $4.25 and then adding 35¢.
     - Slide the dollars over to the first set, write the total down, then slide the cents over and write the total down.
     - Write an arrow diagram.

$4.25 + $3.35

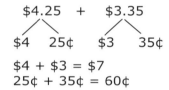

2. Discuss **tasks 4-5, text p. 43**.
   - Do some additional examples. You may wish to include some where the second set includes dollar amounts and the cents add to $1, such as $2.60 + $4.40.

3. If your students are competent in mental math techniques, you may also show them how to add sets of money in which the cents add to more than $1 by making $1. This can be used in situations where it is easy to "make 100" with one of the sets of cents by subtracting that amount from the other set.

$5.65 + $1.45
Add the $1 to $5.65:
$5.65 + $1.45 = $6.65 + 45¢
The difference between 65 and 100 is 35.
Take 35¢ from the 45¢ to make $1 and increase the dollar amount by one. Add the remaining cents.

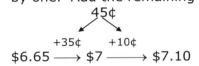

Workbook Exercise 32

Activity 3.2c   **Game**

Material for each group:
*   Store cards.

Procedure:
*   Place cards face up in the center.
*   A student mentally selects two cards (without picking them up or indicating his or her selection) and finds the sum of the price on the two cards.
*   The student tells the others the sum.
*   The other students must guess which two items were selected.
*   Repeat, with students taking turns.

Activity 3.2d   **Add money with the addition algorithm**

1. Discuss adding money using the addition algorithm.
    *   Write an addition problem where the cents will add to more than $1, such as $3.75 + $2.85.
        o   Rewrite the problem vertically. Ask students how many cents there are in $3.75 and in $2.85.
        o   Rewrite the problems without the decimal. Step through the addition using the formal addition algorithm, adding ones first, then tens, then hundreds.

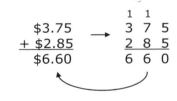

o   The sum is 760 cents. Ask them for the sum in dollars and cents. Tell them when they rewrite the problem vertically, they can align the "dot" for both amounts, and add as they would whole numbers.

2. Discuss **task 6, text p. 44**.
    *   Provide additional problems, including some where the cents are not just multiples of 5.

Workbook Exercise 33

Activity 3.2e   **Mental strategies**

1. Illustrate adding money by adding a whole number of dollars and then subtracting the difference.
   - Display a set of money, such as $3.70, and a separate set of coins of close to $1, such as 95¢.
     - Point out that the 95¢ is almost $1.
     - Ask for the difference between 95¢ and $1.
     - Lead the students to see that they can add $1 and then subtract the 5¢ to get the sum. Write the equation.

$$\$3.70 + 95¢$$
$$95¢ = \$1 - 5¢$$
$$\$3.70 \xrightarrow{+\$1} \$4.70 \xrightarrow{-5¢} \$4.65$$

   - Display two sets of money with both coins and bills where one set has almost a whole dollar in coins, such as $3.45 and $4.97.
     - Discuss various ways of adding these amounts.
     - Lead students to see that they can add $5 and then subtract 3¢.

$$\$3.45 + \$4.97$$
$$4.97¢ = \$5 - 3¢$$
$$\$3.45 \xrightarrow{+\$5} \$8.45 \xrightarrow{-3¢} \$8.42$$

2. Discuss **tasks 7-8, text p. 44**.
   - Provide students with additional practice, involving mental addition of money within $10. Include some problems where the cents are not a multiple of 5. You can use Mental Math 19 on the next page of this guide.

Workbook Exercise 38

Activity 3.2f   **Word problems**

1. Discuss **tasks 9-10, text p. 45**.
   - Provide some additional word problems. You can use the store cards for inspiration. For example, pick up a card and say you bought the item, and have a certain amount of money left. Students add to find out how much you started with.

Workbook Exercise 39

Activity 3.2g   **Store**

1. Use a store theme to get students to practice adding money. Set up a store in the class, using store cards or putting price tags on items in the classroom.
   - Have half students act as cashiers, and half as shoppers. Or, students can also work in small groups, each group with store cards, and one cashier.
   - Give each cashier some coins and bills for change.
   - Give each shopper $10.
     - Shoppers select two items to purchase. They must record the items and find the total amount of money they need to spend.
     - Or, shopper can choose as many items as they can afford. They record all the items and find the total amount of money they need to spend.
   - Shoppers bring their items and $10 to the cashier, who must total the items up and give change.
   - Shoppers need to make sure they get the correct change.

Mental Math 19

1. 65¢ + _____¢ = $1

2. 75¢ + _____¢ = $1

3. $3.75 + $_____ = $10

4. $8.15 + $_____ = $10

5. 41¢ + _____¢ = $1

6. 93¢ + _____¢ = $1

7. $5.08 + $_____ = $10

8. $5.30 + $2 = $_____

9. $2.65 + $6 = $_____

10. $7.32 + $2 = $_____

11. $6.35 + 40¢ = $_____

12. $3.31 + 52¢ = $_____

13. $8.21 + 79¢ = $_____

14. $2.65 + $6.10 = $_____

15. $3.21 + $1.17 = $_____

16. $6.35 + 99¢ = $_____

17. $5.37 + $0.95 = $_____

18. $2.15 + $0.97 = $_____

19. $7.05 + $1.97 = $_____

20. $5.98 + $1.25 = $_____

21. $4.95 + $2.97 = $_____

22. $3.05 + $0.99 = $_____

23. $3.58 + $3.96 = $_____

24. $3.25 + $1.75 = $_____

25. $6.35 + 15¢ = $_____

26. $2.30 + $3.55 = $_____

27. $1.75 + $4.50 = $_____

28. 65¢ + $_____ = $1

29. 65¢ + $_____ = $2

30. 65¢ + $_____ = $10

Part 3: Subtracting Money (pp. 46-51)   **6 sessions**

Objectives

- Subtract money within $100.
- Solve word problems involving the subtraction of money.

Materials

- Play money
- Displayable bills and coins
- Store cards – index cards with pictures of items with a price of less than $10 (use multiples of 5 for the cents)

Homework

- Workbook Exercise 35
- Workbook Exercise 36
- Workbook Exercise 37
- Workbook Exercise 38
- Workbook Exercise 39

Notes

Students will learn the following strategies for subtracting money within $10.

<u>Subtract the dollars and then the cents</u>. For example, to find the difference between $8.75 and $3.50, we first find the difference between $8 and $3, and then between 75¢ and 50¢. The problems at this level will only use multiples of 5 for the cents to facilitate mental addition. They will be able to subtract the cents mentally.

<u>Use the formal algorithm for subtraction</u>. Write the problem vertically, aligning the dots (decimals) and subtract using the same methods as with whole numbers. Students can use the formal algorithm when they cannot solve the problem mentally.

<u>Subtract from a whole number of dollars</u>. This method can be used when it is easy to make 100 with the cents.

$$\$6 - 85¢$$
$$\$5 \quad \$1 - 85¢ = 15¢$$
$$\$5.15$$

<u>Subtract a whole number of dollars, and add the difference</u>. This method can be used when the cents in one set of money is close to 100.

$$\$6.25 - 2.95¢$$
$$\$6.25 \xrightarrow{-\$3} \$3.25 \xrightarrow{+5¢} \$3.30$$

Activity 3.3a   **Subtract cents or dollars**

1. Illustrate subtracting dollars from dollars and cents.
    -   Display a set of money less than $10. Ask students to count the money and then subtract a given number of dollars from it.
    -   After they give you the answer remove the corresponding number of dollars. You may want to use a $5 bill and rename it as five $1 bills to subtract the dollars.
    -   Have them write the subtraction equation.

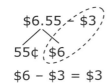

$6 – $3 = $3

$6.55 – $3 = $3.55

2. Illustrate subtracting cents from dollars and cents.
    -   Display a set of money less than $10. Ask the students to count the money and then subtract a given number of cents from it (not more than the number of cents present).
    -   After they give you the answer remove the corresponding number of cents.
    -   Have them write the equation.

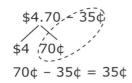

70¢ – 35¢ = 35¢

$4.70 – 35¢ = $4.35

3. Illustrate subtracting money by subtracting the dollars and cents separately.
    -   Display a set of money less than $10. Ask students to count the money.
    -   Write down an amount in dollars and cents to be subtracted (the amount of cents to be subtracted should be less than the amount there).
    -   Ask students to find the dollars in the answer and then the cents.
    -   Have them write the equation

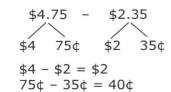

$4 – $2 = $2
75¢ – 35¢ = 40¢

$4.75 – $2.35 = $2.40

4. Illustrate subtracting money from a whole number of dollars.
    -   Display some bills less than $10.
    -   Write down an amount in cents less than 100¢ and ask students to subtract a given amount of cents from it.
    -   Move aside one of the dollars and show how they can subtract from that dollar using mental math strategies for making 100.
    -   Have them write the equation.

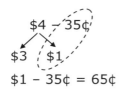

$1 – 35¢ = 65¢

$4 – 35¢ = $3.65

5. Discuss **text p. 46** and **tasks 1-3, p 47**.

Workbook Exercise 35

Activity 3.3b   **Subtract dollars and cents**

1. Illustrate subtracting money by subtracting the dollars first and then the cents.
   - Display a set of money, such as $6.80.
     - ○ Write the expression $6.80 - $3.35.
     - ○ Tell students they find the answer by first subtracting $3 from $6.80 and then subtracting 35¢.
     - ○ Remove first $3 and then 35¢ and write the arrow diagram on the board.
     - ○ Have students write the equation.

$6.80 – $3.35

$$\begin{array}{ccc} & -\$3 & -35¢ \\ \$6.80 \longrightarrow & \$3.80 \longrightarrow & \$3.45 \end{array}$$

$6.80 - $3.35 = $3.45

2. Discuss **tasks 4-5, text p. 47**.
   - Provide additional problems for practice.

3. If your students are competent in mental math techniques, you may also show them how to subtract mentally by subtracting the dollars and then subtracting from a whole number of dollars. This can be used in situations where it is easy to "make 100" with the amount being subtracted.

$5.45 – $1.75
Subtract the $1 from $5.45:
$5.45 – $1.75 = $4.45 – 75¢
The difference between 100 and 75 is 25.
Reduce the dollar amount by another dollar, and add the 25¢.

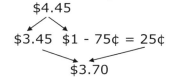

$4.45
$3.45 $1 - 75¢ = 25¢
$3.70

Workbook Exercise 36

Activity 3.3c   **Game**

Material for each group:
- Store cards.

Procedure:
- Place cards face up in the center.
- A student mentally selects two cards (without picking them up or indicating his or her selection) and finds the difference in the price on the two cards.
- The student tells the others the difference.
- The other students must guess which two items were selected.
- Repeat, with students taking turns.

Activity 3.3d   **Subtract money using the subtraction algorithm**

1. Discuss subtracting money using the addition algorithm.
   - Write a subtraction problem where a dollar will have to be renamed to subtract the cents, such as $5.60 – $2.85.
     - ○ Rewrite the problem vertically and then without the decimal to show the amount in cents.
     - ○ Step through the subtraction using the formal subtraction algorithm, subtracting ones first, then tens, then hundreds.

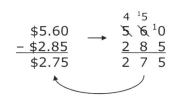

- o Tell them when they write the problem vertically, they can align the "dot" for both amounts, and then subtract as they would whole numbers.

2. Discuss **task 6, text p. 48**.
   - Provide some additional problems, including some where the cents are not just multiples of 5.

Workbook Exercise 37

Activity 3.3e   **Mental strategies**

1. Illustrate subtracting money by subtracting a whole number of dollars and then adding back the difference.
   - Display a set of money, such as $3.70.
     - o Tell students you want to subtract 95¢. Write the equation.
     - o Discuss strategies for subtracting 95¢. Lead the students to see that one strategy they can use is to subtract a whole dollar. Since that means they are subtracting 5¢ to much, they have to add that back in.

$3.70 – 95¢
$1 = 95¢ + 5¢

$$\overset{-\$1}{\$3.70 \longrightarrow \$2.70} \overset{+5¢}{\longrightarrow \$2.75}$$

   - Display a set of money, such as $7.45.
     - o Tell students you want to subtract $4.97. Discuss various ways of subtracting these amounts.
     - o Lead students to see that they can subtract $5 and then add back in 3¢.

$7.45 – $4.97
$5 =$4.97 + 3¢

$$\overset{-\$5}{\$7.45 \longrightarrow \$2.45} \overset{+3¢}{\longrightarrow \$2.48}$$

2. Discuss **tasks 7-8, text p. 48.**
   - Provide students with additional practice, involving mental addition of money within $10. Include some problems where the cents are not a multiple of 5. You can use Mental Math 20 on the next page of this guide.

Mental Math 20

1. $8.30 – $4 = $_____

2. $4.15 – $2 = $_____

3. $9.66 – $5 = $_____

4. $1 – 75¢ = $_____

5. $6 – 45¢ = $_____

6. $8 – 23¢ = $_____

7. $10 – 65¢ = $_____

8. $10 – $3.10 = $_____

9. $4.70 – $1.15 = $_____

10. $8.80 – $4.25 = $_____

11. $8.88 – $4.26 = $_____

12. $5.70 – $2.25 = $_____

13. $5.90 – $0.99 = $_____

14. $4.55 – $0.95 = $_____

15. $3.21 – $0.97 = $_____

16. $6.35 – $4.96 = $_____

17. $7.05 – $1.97 = $_____

18. $4.95 – $2.96 = $_____

19. $5.98 – $1.25 = $_____

20. $10 – $4.15 = $_____

21. $6.00 – $0.12 = $_____

22. $6.00 – $3.12 = $_____

23. $4 – 99¢ = $_____

24. $42 – $8 = $_____

25. $95 – $25 = $_____

26. $100 – $46 = $_____

27. $8.25 – $0.95 = $_____

28. $8.25 – $0.90 = $_____

29. $8.25 – $0.85 = $_____

30. $8.25 – $0.55 = $_____

Activity 3.3f   **Word problems**

1. Discuss **tasks 9-10, text p. 49**.
   • Provide some additional word problems. You can use the store cards for inspiration. For example, pick up a card and say you want to buy the item and have $9. How much change will you receive?

Workbook Exercise 29

Activity 3.3g   **Game**

Material for each group:
• Store cards

Procedure:
Shuffle cards and place them in the middle, face down.
• Students write $10 on their paper.
• They take turns drawing two cards each.
• First they find the difference between the items on the cards.
• They record the items and the difference in cost.
• Repeat 2 more times. They will have 3 differences recorded. Students then add their three values together.
• The student with the highest sum wins.

Activity 3.3h   **Practice**

1. Use **text p. 50, Practice 3B** and **text p. 51, Practice 3C** to review the unit.

Unit 4 – Fractions

Objectives

- Understand fractional notation.
- Identify and write fractions of a whole.
- Compare and order unit fractions.
- Find fractions whose sum makes a whole.

Suggested number of sessions: 5

	Objectives	Textbook	Workbook	Activities
Part 1 : Halves and Quarters				**1 session**
	Objectives	**Textbook**	**Workbook**	**Activities**
45	▪ Recognize and name half and quarter. ▪ Read and write half and quarter in fractional notation $\frac{1}{2}$ and $\frac{1}{4}$.	pp. 52-53 p. 53, tasks 1-2	Ex. 40	4.1a
Part 2 : Writing Fractions				**4 sessions**
46	▪ Understand fractional notation. ▪ Identify and write different	p. 54 p. 55, tasks 1-2	Ex. 41	4.2a
47	▪ fractions of a whole. ▪ Name unit fractions up to $\frac{1}{12}$	p. 56, tasks 3-4	Ex. 42 Ex. 43	4.2b
48	▪ Compare and order unit fractions	p. 57, tasks 5-6	Ex. 44	4.2c 4.2d
49	▪ Find fractions whose sum makes a whole.	p. 57, task 7	Ex. 45	4.2e 4.2f

Part 1: Halves and Quarters (pp. 52-53)	1 session

Objectives

- Recognize and name halves and quarters.
- Read and write the fraction notations $\frac{1}{2}$ and $\frac{1}{4}$.

Materials

- Paper strips
- Plain sheets of letter-sized paper or smaller
- Paper squares
- Paper circles

Homework

- Workbook Exercise 40

Notes

Students learned the concepts of halves and quarters in *Primary Mathematics 1B*. This is reviewed here. Students will be introduced to the notation $\frac{1}{2}$ and $\frac{1}{4}$. They should understand that $\frac{1}{2}$ of a whole means one out of two equal parts and $\frac{1}{4}$ of a whole means one out of four equal parts. Two halves make a whole and four quarters make a whole.

Activity 4.1a $\dfrac{1}{2}$ and $\dfrac{1}{4}$

1. Review halves and quarters.
   - Give each student two strips of paper.
     - Ask them to cut the first strip one into two equal parts. Check results. Tell them each part is one half. To be a half of the whole, each half needs to be the same size. Ask them how many halves make a whole.
     - Ask them to cut the second strip into four equal parts. Let them do it their own way. They should check that all their pieces are the same size. Tell them each part is a quarter. It is also called a fourth.
   - Give students some sheets of paper.
     - Show students how to fold the sheet in half by lining up the edges and corners. Have them color one half.
     - Write the symbol $\dfrac{1}{2}$ and have them copy it onto the colored half of their paper.
     - Tell them this is read as "one half" and means one out of two equal parts of a whole. The whole, or total, is the rectangle (not a "hole").
     - Let them experiment with dividing the paper in half in other ways. They can cut apart the halves and then lay one on top of the other to see if they are the same size.
     - Draw some rectangles on the board and divide some unevenly. Ask if each part is one half.
     - Show students how to fold a sheet of paper in quarters by first folding in half and then in half again. Have them color one quarter.
     - Write the symbol $\dfrac{1}{4}$ and have them copy it onto the colored half of their paper.
     - Tell them this is read as "one fourth" or "one quarter" and means one out of four equal parts of a whole.
     - Have them fold another paper in half and color $\dfrac{1}{2}$, then fold again and color $\dfrac{1}{4}$ with a different color. Ask them which is larger. The paper is divided into fewer parts for $\dfrac{1}{2}$ than for $\dfrac{1}{4}$. Point out that $\dfrac{1}{2}$ and $\dfrac{1}{4}$ are fractions *of a whole*. To compare them to each other, the whole must be the same. For example, we can compare $\dfrac{1}{2}$ and $\dfrac{1}{4}$ of a pizza, but we can't compare $\dfrac{1}{4}$ of a pizza to $\dfrac{1}{2}$ of a slice of bread. $\dfrac{1}{2}$ *of the pizza* (not the *bread*) is larger than $\dfrac{1}{4}$ *of the pizza*.
   - Repeat with paper circles or squares. Let students fold to divide into halves and quarters, and color one half or one quarter. Have them choose one showing a half and one showing a fourth where they have folded the shape in the same way (such as along the diagonal for a square).

2. Discuss **text p. 52 and tasks 1-2, text p. 53**.

Workbook Exercise 40

Part 2: Writing Fractions (pp. 54-57)   **4 sessions**

Objectives

- Understand fractional notation.
- Identify and write fractions of a whole.
- Compare and order unit fractions.
- Find fractions whose sum makes a whole.

Materials

- Connect-A-Cubes and Connect-a-Cube GEO shapes.
- Displayable color squares
- Blank fraction strips for students (copy the next page onto cardstock; cut strips apart of have students cut the strips, see activity 4.2c)
- Displayable basic fraction tiles (2 sets, cut up the strips for one set)
- Displayable fraction circles with grids
- Displayable fraction squares with grids
- Fraction cards (see activity 4.2d and 4.2f)

Homework

- Workbook Exercise 41
- Workbook Exercise 42
- Workbook Exercise 43
- Workbook Exercise 44
- Workbook Exercise 45

Notes

Students have already learned about part-whole in both addition and multiplication. In addition, two or more unequal parts can make the whole, or total. In multiplication, a given number of equal parts make the whole, or total.

Fractions also represent a part-whole relationship. The fraction notation tells how much of the whole the part represents. $\frac{1}{4}$ represents 1 out of 4 equal parts of the whole. $\frac{3}{4}$ represent 3 out of 4 equal parts. Students will later learn that the whole can be any amount, such as 24, and will find $\frac{1}{4}$ of the whole by first finding the value of each equal part using division. Right now, the whole is simply one unit, whether a fraction bar or a circle. The more parts the whole is divided into, the smaller the part. A unit fraction is one of the parts. $\frac{1}{4}$ and $\frac{1}{6}$ are unit fractions. We can compare unit fractions by comparing the denominator. $\frac{1}{6}$ is smaller than $\frac{1}{4}$ because the part of the whole is smaller.

Do not use the terms denominator and numerator yet. These will be taught at a later level.

Blank Fraction Strips

Activity 4.2a   **Write fractions**

1. Illustrate fractions, fractional notation, and fractions of a whole using fraction circles.
   - Display a whole circle and say that this is the whole. Show 3 thirds and put them on top of the circle to form a whole. Ask how many parts there are.

   - Remove two of the pieces. Tell students that the remaining piece is one part out of three equal parts.
   - Write $\frac{1}{3}$ and tell students that this means one out of three equal parts. It is read as "one third."
   - Add another third to the circle and ask how many thirds there are. This is 2 parts out of the three equal parts that make the whole

   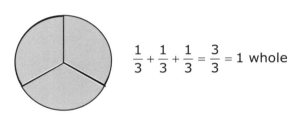

   - Write $\frac{2}{3} = \frac{1}{3} + \frac{1}{3}$.
   - Add the last third to the circle. Ask how many thirds there are. Ask how many thirds are there in one whole.
   - Write $\frac{1}{3} + \frac{1}{3} + \frac{1}{3} = \frac{3}{3} = 1$ whole .
   - Repeat with another fraction, such as $\frac{1}{6}$, using a different shape for the whole, such as a fraction square or fraction strip. Add one sixth at a time, writing the new fraction as a sum of sixths.
   - Write some fractions up to 12/12, and ask students to name them. Except for one half, we say the top number as a regular counting number, and the bottom the same way we say the position in line (e.g. third, fourth, fifth). So $\frac{3}{5}$ is "three fifths." A four on the bottom can be either fourths or quarters. $\frac{3}{4}$ can be either "three fourths" or "three quarters."

2. Discuss **text, p. 54** and **tasks 1-2, text p. 55**.
   - Have students read the sentences on page 55 out loud, naming the fractions correctly.

Workbook Exercise 41

Activity 4.2b

Fractions of a whole

1. Illustrate fractions with other shapes.
   - Draw a bar or other shape on the board and divide it into fractions, such as eighths. Color several non-contiguous parts of it.
     - Ask students what fraction of the whole is colored. Write the fraction.
     - Point out that the top number is the number of parts that is colored, and the bottom is the total number of parts. Make sure students don't make the mistake of writing the number of uncolored parts for the bottom number in the fraction notation.
     - Color in a few other sections and ask for the fraction that is colored.

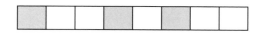

$\dfrac{3}{8}$ of the bar is shaded.

2. Discuss **tasks 3-4, text p. 56**. Have students write and name the fractions.

3. Have students use connect-a-cubes and geo-shapes to make similar objects of up to 12 units of two or more colors and write down the fraction of the total that is a particular color.
   - Students can pair up. One student makes the shape and the other determines what fraction of the total shape is a certain color.

Workbook Exercises 43-43

Activity 4.2c

Compare and order unit fractions

1. Illustrate comparing unit fractions.
   - Tell students that 6 people want to share a pizza. Draw one on the board and divide it into 6 pieces. Then tell them 4 people want to share a pizza of the same size.
     - Draw another pizza on the board and divide it into 4 pieces. Ask who would get a larger piece, someone in the first group or someone in the second group? Why? Since the first pizza has to be cut up into more pieces, each piece is smaller.
     - Write $\dfrac{1}{4}$ is greater than $\dfrac{1}{6}$.
   - Provide each student with a set of fraction strips.
     - Have students color one part of each strip on the left side and write the fraction the colored part represents. Then have students use the strips to find out which is smaller, $\dfrac{1}{8}$ or $\dfrac{1}{10}$. Do some other examples.
     - Lead students to see that the more parts there are, the smaller each part is.

$\dfrac{1}{4}$ is greater than $\dfrac{1}{6}$

2. Discuss **tasks 5-6, text p. 57**. students can use the fraction strips for task 6.
   - List all the unit fractions from $\dfrac{1}{2}$ to $\dfrac{1}{12}$ on the board in random order. Have students read the fractions. Ask them to list them in their journals from smallest to largest.

Workbook Exercise 44

Activity 4.2d   **Game**

Material for each group of an even number of students:

- Two or three sets of fraction cards $\frac{1}{2}, \frac{1}{3}, \frac{1}{4}, \frac{1}{5}, \frac{1}{6}, \frac{1}{7}, \frac{1}{8}, \frac{1}{9}, \frac{1}{10}, \frac{1}{11}, \frac{1}{12}$.

Procedure:
- Shuffle cards and deal all out.
- Students take turns drawing a card or turns over one of their cards.
- The one with the largest fraction gets all the cards that have been turned over. If there is a tie they each get half the cards turned over.
- Play continues until all cards have been turned over.
- The student with the most cards wins.

Activity 4.2e   **Fractions that make a whole**

1. Illustrate fractions that make a whole.
    - Draw or display a fraction circle grid, square, or bar.
        - Color in part of it. Ask students for the fraction that is colored.
        - Then ask students for the fraction that is not colored. Ask what both fractions together make.
        - Write the two fractions that make a whole. Ask students to add the top numbers (the number of parts) together and compare the sum to the bottom number.
    - Repeat with a few other examples.

$\frac{4}{9}$ and $\frac{5}{9}$ make 1 whole

2. Discuss **task 7, text p. 57**.
    - Write some fractions on the board and ask students for the fraction that makes a whole with it.

Workbook Exercise 44

Activity 4.2f   **Game**

Material for each group of students:
- A set of fraction cards with the following fractions:

$\frac{1}{2}, \frac{1}{2}, \frac{1}{3}, \frac{2}{3}, \frac{1}{4}, \frac{2}{4}, \frac{2}{4}, \frac{3}{4}, \frac{1}{5}, \frac{2}{5}, \frac{3}{5}, \frac{4}{5}, \frac{1}{6}, \frac{2}{6}, \frac{3}{6}, \frac{3}{6}, \frac{4}{6}, \frac{5}{6}, \frac{1}{7}, \frac{2}{7}, \frac{3}{7}, \frac{4}{7}, \frac{5}{7}, \frac{6}{7},$
$\frac{1}{8}, \frac{2}{8}, \frac{3}{8}, \frac{4}{8}, \frac{4}{8}, \frac{5}{8}, \frac{6}{8}, \frac{7}{8}, \frac{1}{9}, \frac{2}{9}, \frac{3}{9}, \frac{4}{9}, \frac{5}{9}, \frac{6}{9}, \frac{7}{9},$ and $\frac{8}{9}$.

Procedure:
- Shuffle cards and place in a pile face down in the middle.
- Turn over the top one is turned over and place it face-up in the playing area.
- Students take turns turning over the next card and trying to pair it with a face-up card to make 1 whole. If they can, the two cards are removed from play. If not, the new card is left face up in the playing enter.
- Play continues until all cards are paired.

Review

Objectives

- Review all topics.

Suggested number of sessions: 2

	Objectives	Textbook	Workbook	Activity
50	▪ Review.	p. 58, Review B	Review 3	R.2
51		p. 59, Review C	Review 4	

Activity R.2   Review

1. Use **Review B, text p. 58** and **Review C, text p. 59** to review topics covered so far. Call on students to supply the answers and explain their work for the word problems.

2. Provide additional review as necessary. You can use Mental Math worksheets and games from units 1-4.

Workbook Review 3
Workbook Review 4

Unit 5 – Time

Objectives

- Tell time to the 5 minute interval.
- Find time intervals using a clock face.
- Use a.m. and p.m.
- Find start or end time of a time interval.

Suggested number of sessions: 6

	Objectives	Textbook	Workbook	Activity
Part 1 : Telling Time				**3 sessions**
52	• Tell time to the 5-minute interval. • Read time notation. • Tell time as minutes after the hour.	pp. 60-61	Ex. 46	5.1a
53	• Tell time as minutes before the hour. • Tell time to the quarter hour.	p. 62, task 1	Ex. 47, #1-2	5.1b
54	• Relate time to events of the day. • Use a.m. and p.m.	p. 63, task 2	Ex. 47, #3	5.1c
Part 2 : Time Intervals				**3 sessions**
55	• Find the duration of a time interval in minutes using a clock face.	pp. 64 p. 66, task 1		5.2a
56	• Find the duration of a time interval in hours using a clock face.	pp. 66-67, tasks 2-4	Ex. 48	5.2b
57	• Find the start or end time for a time intervals.	p. 67, tasks 5-6 p. 68, Practice 5A	Ex. 49	5.2c

Part 1: Telling Time (pp. 60-62)   3 sessions

Objectives

- Tell time to the 5 minute interval.
- Relate time to events of the day.
- Use the abbreviations a.m. and p.m.

Materials

- Classroom Clock Kit
- Analog/Digital Clock Face Stamp
- Worksheets (see activity 5.1a)

Homework

- Workbook Exercise 46
- Workbook Exercise 47

Notes

Students learned to tell time to the hour and half-hour in *Primary Mathematics 1B*. They learned to read and say the time as *4 o'clock* or *half past 4*. Here, they will learn to tell time to the five-minute interval, and to read and write time using the hour:minutes notation (e.g. 7:05).

Note for 3rd edition: In the U.S. a colon is used between the hours and minutes. That convention will be used in this guide. You may substitute the convention used in your country.

Students may be more familiar with a digital clock. An analog clock, or "face" clock, will give them a visual picture of time and the fraction of an hour that has passed. It is also useful in determining time intervals.

Use a classroom demonstration clock and individual student clock where the hands are geared and move in relation to each other.

Students will learn the abbreviation a.m. (ante-meridiem) for before noon, and p.m. (post-meridiem) for after noon.

Activity 5.1a   **Tell time as minutes after the hour**

1. Review the clock face, hours, and half-hours.
   • Provide each student with a small geared clock and have them follow the discussion while you use a large classroom geared clock.
   • Remind students which hand is the hour hand and which is the minute hand. Ask students what the numbers around the clock mean.
   • Set the time for 12:00 and move the minute hand all the way around. Ask students how far the hour hand goes when the minute hand goes all the way around. One hour passes as the minute hand goes around, and the hour changes to the next hour.
   • Let students experiment with their clocks. Have students tell you some events that take about an hour.

2. Review telling time to the hour and the half-hour.
   • Set the time to an hour, such as 4:00, and ask students for the time. They have learned this as "4 o'clock" in Primary Mathematics 1B.
   • Move the hand around half-way. Ask students how far around the hand moved. Ask them for the time. They have learned this is "half past 4".
   • Ask them to set their clocks for given times on the hour or half-hour.

3. Discuss minutes.
   • Have students count the number of small intervals between two numbers marked by the small lines. Tell them when the minute hand moves from one small mark to the next it has moved 1 minute. There are 5 minutes between one number (larger mark) and the next.
   • Start the minute hand at 12 and have the students count by 5 as you move it from number to number. Lead them to see that there are 60 minutes in an hour.
   • Ask student to name some activities that last a minute. Use a stopwatch and time some activity, such as hopping in place, for 1 minute.

4. Discuss writing time using the hour:minutes notation and time to the five minutes.
   • Set the time on an hour, such as 6:00 and ask students for the time.
     o Write the time on the board using the digital notation.
     o Tell students that this is how we can write 6 o'clock. The two dots are called a colon. The number before the colon is the hour. The number after the colon is the minutes. When the minute hand is straight up, no minutes have passed for the hour yet, so the minutes are 00.
   • Move the minute hand to the 1.
     o Ask how many minutes this is.
     o Write the time as 6:05.
     o Tell student we read this as "six oh five" and it means "5 minutes after 6 o'clock", or "5 minutes past 6". Point out that as with money (e.g. the cents in $6.05) we need to have two digits for the minutes, so if there are no tens we put in 0 as a place holder.

6:00
6 o'clock

6:05
"six oh five"
"five minutes past 6"

- Continue around the clock for every five minutes. Point out that the hour hand is moving slowly around as well, and that at 6:30 it is halfway to the 7. 6:30 is read as "six thirty" and is "30 minutes after 6" or "half past six".
- Set the time at various times (multiples of 5) and have the students read and write the time in the digital format.
- Write some times in the digital format on the board and have the students set the correct times on their clocks. Then set the time on your clock and have them check it against their clocks.

6:45

4. Discuss **text pp. 60-61** (except for bottom two lines on p. 61).

Workbook Exercise 46

Activity 5.1b   **Tell time as minutes before the hour**

1. Discuss telling time as minutes before the hour.
    - Provide each student with a small geared clock and have them follow the discussion while you use a large classroom geared clock.
    - Review telling time as minutes after the hour up until half past the hour, such as 2:30. Set the clock for 2:05 and ask for the time, then 2:10, and so on up to 2:30
    - Tell students this is also 30 minutes to 3. Count by fives from the 6 to 12 to show that there are 30 more minutes to go.
    - Move the minute hand to 2:35, write the time, and have students count by fives from the minute hand position to the 12.
    - Tell them that this time can also be given as "25 minutes before 3 o'clock" or 25 minutes to 3". Continue with 2:40, 2:45, 2:50, and 2:55.

2:35
35 minutes past 2
25 minutes to 3

2. Discuss quarter hours.
    - Draw a circle and divide it into quarters. Write 12, 3, 6, and 9 at each quarter.
    - Use the clock and set the time at 12:00. Ask for the time.
    - Move the minute hand to 3. Outline the quarter circle with your finger. Tell students that the minute hand has moved a quarter of the way around. This time is also called "a quarter past 12".

12:15
a quarter past 12

- Move the minute hand to the 9. Ask students for the time. This time is "twelve forty-five", "15 minutes to 1", or "a quarter to one".

12:45
a quarter to 1

- Set the time at various times (multiples of 5) and have the students read and write the digital time. For times after the half hour, have them give the time as the number of minutes to the next hour.
- Name or write some times before the hour, such as 20 minutes to 3, or a quarter to 8, and have the students set the time on their clocks and check against yours. They can also write the digital time.

3. Discuss **text p. 61,** last item, and **task 1, p. 62**.

Workbook Exercise 47, problems 1-2

Activity 5.1c   **Time of day**

1. Relate time to events of the day. Use a demonstration clock
    - Set the time to 12:00.
    - Tell students that 12:00 is the time in the middle of the night, and is called midnight.
    - Ask some students when they get up in the morning and move the time to that time. Continue with other activities until 12:00 noon. Tell students that this is the middle of the day, and is called 12 noon.
    - Continue with activities in the afternoon and evening until bed time. Then move the time to 12:00 again. This is now 12 midnight again. A day is from one 12 midnight to the next.
    - Ask students how many hours are in a day. There are 24 hours, in two sets of 12. You may want to tell students that in military time, and in other countries, 1:00 p.m. is 13:00, 2:00 p.m. is 14:00, etc.

2. Discuss a.m. and p.m.
    - Ask students what they do at 8:00 in the morning and at 8:00 in the evening. Tell them that since the same time shows twice on the clock in a day, we use a.m. and p.m. to tell whether the time is before noon or after noon.
    - Show how these are written. Write some times with a.m. or p.m. on the board and ask what the students might be doing at those particular times.

3. Discuss **task 2, text p. 63**.
    - Have students write the times shown. Ask them whether they would put a.m. or p.m. after the time.

Workbook Exercise 47, problem 3

Part 2: Time Intervals (pp. 64-69)   **3 sessions**

Objectives

- Find the duration of a time interval using a clock face.
- Find the start or end time of a time interval.

Materials

- Classroom Clock Kit
- Analog/Digital Clock Face Stamp

Homework

- Workbook Exercise 48
- Workbook Exercise 49

Notes

Students will be learning how to determine the duration of a time interval in either hours or minutes in this section. They will always have the use of a clock face to help them at this level. In *Primary Mathematics 3* they will learn to find the duration without a clock face.

The times in this unit are all multiples of 5. Students will probably be able to easily tell time to the minute, as well, but they can also tell time to the nearest 5 minutes (e.g. *about* 2:25 for 2:23) rather than counting the minutes between each 5-minute interval. If you have a clock face in the classroom, have them periodically tell you the time on it to the nearest 5 minutes.

Activity 5.2a   **Elapsed time in minutes**

1. Illustrate how to find the number of minutes that have passed from one time to another with clock faces.
   - Provide students with small geared clocks while you use the large demonstration clock. The start and end times of all these activities should be a multiple of 5. Students can work in pairs so that one can set the start time and the other the end time.
   - Pick a familiar activity of less than 1 hour, such as a TV show, that has a specific start and end time.

     - Write down the start and end times.
     - Have one student of each pair set the start time on their clock and the other set the end time.
     - The student with the start time then counts by fives for each number from the start time to the end time they move the minute hand of their clock to match the end time on their partner's clock.

   start 2:10   end 2:35
   5, 10, 15, 20, 25
   time passed = 25 minutes

     - Have them tell you the number of minutes for how long the activity lasts.
   - Do a few other examples, with the students changing roles.
   - Do some other examples where the students work individually. They can do this in various ways. They can put their finger at the start time, move the minute hand to the end time, and then count the five minute intervals, or they can form a mental image of the end time and move the hands as they count, or they can put their finger where the minute hand would be at the end time and count the intervals.

2. Discuss **text p. 64** and **task 1, text p. 65**.

3. Guide students in understanding that 30 minutes is half-way around the clock, even for other start times than a time on the hour or half-hour:
   - Write a time, such as 4:10.
     - Have one student in each pair set their clocks to this time. Set the demonstration clock to this time.

     - Write a time exactly 30 minutes later. Have the second student set their clock for this time.
     - Put your finger to the position the minute hand would be on the demonstration clock so they can see the start time and the end time on the same clock.

   start 4:10   end 4:40
   time passed = 30 minutes

     - Lead them to see that the minute hand has moved half way around. Ask students for the number of minutes that have passed.
   - Repeat with a few other examples where the elapsed time is 30 minutes.

4. Have students find elapsed time as 5 minutes less or more than half-way around the clock:
   - Show and write a time, such as 4:10.
     - Keep your finger at the 2, where the minute hand is, and move the hand half way around (to 4:40). If you have two demonstration clocks, you can set one time on the

first clock and the other time on the second clock. Ask students how much time has passed.

- o Then move the minute hand back 5 minutes (to 4:35) and write the time. Ask students how much time has passed from the original time. Lead them to see that since it is 5 minutes back from half way around, they can find the time that has passed as 5 less than 30 minutes.
- o Now move the minute hand 5 minutes forward from 4:40 (to 4:45). Ask students how much time has passed since the original 4:10. Help them recognize that it is 5 minutes more than half way around, or 5 minutes more than 30 minutes.

5. Provide additional practice.
   - Write some start and end times down and have the students use their clocks to find the time that has passed. Include some times that go from one hour to the next, such as 2:50 to 3:10.

Activity 5.2b   **Elapsed time in hours**

1. Illustrate how to find the number of hours that have passed from one time to another with clock faces.
   - Provide students with small geared clocks while you use the large demonstration clock. The start and end times of all these activities should be a multiple of 5. Students can work in pairs.
   - Show a time to the hour, such as 4:00.
     - o Ask students for the time. Write the time down and have the students set the same time on their clocks.
     - o Move the minute hand all the way around, and ask students for the new time. Write the new time down.
     - o Ask students how much time has passed since 4:00. Point out that the minute hand goes back to the same position, while the hour hand has gone from 4 to 5.

start 4:00   end 6:00
time passed = 2 hours

   - Move the minute hand all the way around again and write the new time down again (6:00).
     - o Ask how much time has passed since 4:00. 6:00 is 2 hours later than 4:00.
   - Repeat with a time that is not on the hour, such as 2:30. Write down the start time.
     - o Move the minute hand around 3 times, so that the new time is 5:30, and write the new time down. Ask students how much time has passed.
     - o Point out again that the hour hand has moved, but the minute hand ends up at the same place.

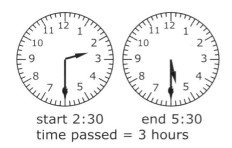

start 2:30   end 5:30
time passed = 3 hours

2. Guide students in finding elapsed time in hours when the time passes 12:00:
   - Ask a student when he or she arrives at school. Set the time for that time, and write it down, followed by a.m. See if the students remember what a.m. means. Have students set their clocks at the same time.

start 8:30 a.m.   end 2:30 p.m.
time passed = 6 hours

- Find some activity that is several hours later and set the new time on the clock, write it down, and ask for the number of hours that have passed.
- Repeat with an activity that occurs several hours later in the afternoon. Write the time down with p.m. Remind students of the meaning of p.m. Ask them how many hours have passed.
- Lead students to see that if they pass 12 when counting the number of hours that have passed; the time will change from a.m. to p.m. (or p.m. to a.m.) so that the hour for the end time may be less than the hour for the start time.

3. Discuss **tasks 2-4, text pp. 66-67**.

4. Provide additional practice
   - Write some start and end times down (same number of minutes) and have the students use their clocks to find the hours that have passed. Include some times that go from a.m. to p.m. or from p.m. to a.m.
   - Provide additional practice as needed.

Workbook Exercise 48

Activity 5.2c   **Start and end times**

1. Show students how to find start and end times given the elapsed time.
   - Provide each student with a small geared clock and have them follow the discussion while you use a large classroom geared clock. The times for all these activities should be multiples of 5.
   - Write a start time for some activity, and the number of hours it lasts.
     - o Ask students for the end time. Allow them to use their clocks to find the end time.
     - o Repeat with other examples.
     - o Write down the start time and the number of hours that have passed and call on students to write the end time.
     - o Include examples where the time starts in the a.m. and ends in the p.m. and vice-versa.
   - Write an end time for some activity, and the number of hours it lasts.
     - o Ask students for the start time. They should realize that they need to move the clock hands backwards (counterclockwise) to find the start time.
     - o Repeat with other examples, including ones that go from a.m. to p.m. or from p.m. to a.m.
   - Write down a start time for an activity and the number of minutes it lasts. The minutes should be less than one hour. Ask students for the end time. Let them use their clocks.
   - Follow a similar procedure to discuss finding start times given end times and the elapsed time in minutes.
   - Repeat with other examples.

2. Discuss **tasks 5-6, text p. 67** and **Practice 5A, text p. 68**.

Workbook Exercise 49

Review

Objectives

- Review all topics.

Suggested number of sessions: 1

	Objectives	Textbook	Workbook	Activity
56	▪ Review.	p. 69, Review D	Review 5	R.3

Activity R.3   Review

1. Use **Review D, text p. 69,** to review topics covered so far. Call on students to supply the answers and explain their work for the word problems.

2. Provide additional review as necessary. You can use Mental Math worksheets and games from previous units.

Workbook Review 5

Unit 6 – Capacity

Objectives

- Understand the term capacity
- Compare the capacity of various containers.
- Understand the liter as a unit of measurement.
- Solve word problems involving capacity.
- ^{US} Understand the gallon, quart, pint, and cup as units of measurement
- ^{US} Compare cup with pint with quart with gallon.
- ^{US} Compare quart with liter.

Suggested number of sessions: 5

	Objectives	Textbook	Workbook	Activity
Part 1 : Comparing Capacity				**1 session**
59	• Compare the capacity of containers.	p. 70 p. 71, tasks 1-2	Ex. 50, 51	6.1a
Part 2 : Liter				**2 sessions**
	Objectives	**Textbook**	**Workbook**	**Activity**
60	• Understand the liter as unit of measurement. • Compare volume in liters.	p. 72 pp. 73-75, tasks 1-6	Ex. 52 ^{US} Ex. 53, #1-2 ^{3d} Ex. 53	6.2a
61	• Solve word problems involving capacity.	p. 76, Practice 6A	^{US} Ex. 53, #3-4 ^{3d} Ex. 54	6.2b
^{US} **Part 3 : Gallons, Quart, Pints and Cups**				**2 sessions**
62	• Understand cups, pints, quarts, and gallons as units of measurement. • Compare the units to each other.	^{US} pp. 77-78 ^{US} pp. 78-80, tasks 1-4		6.3a
63	• Determine an appropriate unit of measurement. • Solve word problems involving capacity.	^{US} p. 80, task 5	^{US} Ex. 54	6.3b

Part 1: Comparing Capacity (pp. 70-71)   **1 session**

Objectives

- Compare the capacity of two or more containers.

Materials

- A large basin to catch water spills, two bottles of the same size, and various containers labeled with A, B, C, etc.
- Water colored with food coloring
- Paper cups or other smaller containers

Homework

- Workbook Exercise 50
- Workbook Exercise 51

Notes

The capacity of a container is how much liquid it will hold.

Students will learn various ways of comparing the capacity of two or more containers. Students should have concrete experience actually filling up and pouring out from various containers.

There are several ways to compare the capacity of two containers.

➢ Fill up one container, and then pour the water from it into the other. If there is some remaining in the first when the second is full, the first has a greater capacity.
➢ Fill up each container, and pour the contents into smaller containers of equal capacity to see how many more small containers one fills than the other.
➢ Fill up both containers and pour the contents into two larger containers of equal size and shape and compare the levels.

Note for 3rd edition: The U.S. spelling for liter will be used in this guide, rather than litre.

Activity 6.1a   **Capacity**

1. Discuss ways to compare the capacity of various containers.
   - Have ready some colored water in a jug, various containers of different capacities labeled A, B, C, etc., two bottles of the same size, and some paper cups.
   - Show students two containers of about equal capacity but different shapes, such as short and wide versus tall and thin.
     o Tell them that the **capacity** of a container is how much liquid it can hold. Ask students which container has the most capacity. They may guess one or the other.
     o Ask them how they can be sure. They may be able to tell just by looking, but they need to come up with a definitive method, since a short squat container may have a greater capacity than a tall skinny one.
     o Have some of the students come up one at a time to demonstrate their ideas.
   - Discuss **text p. 70**. This is one way of comparing the capacity of two containers — they can fill up one container and then pour it into another.
   - Discuss **tasks 1-2, text p. 71**. This is another way of comparing the capacity of two containers — they can fill up each container and then pour the water into smaller containers of equal size to see which fills up the most smaller containers.
   - Discuss a third method, if students have not already suggested it. They can fill up the two containers and then pour the water from each into two larger containers of the same size and compare the level of water. Call on a student to demonstrate this method with two bottles of the same size.
   - Show the students various containers labeled A, B, C, etc.
     o Call on some students to use one of the methods discussed previously to put the containers in order of their capacities.

Workbook Exercises 50-51

Part 2: Liters (pp. 72-75)   **2 sessions**

Objectives

- Understand the liter as a unit of measurement.
- Compare the capacity of containers in liters.
- Estimate and measure the capacity of containers in liters.
- Solve word problems involving liters.

Materials

- A large basin to catch spills, paper cups, some containers of less than, more than, and almost 1 liter capacity, a basin and some other containers such as a kettle and a watering can that can hold several liters
- Colored water
- Paper cups
- Liter beakers or measuring cups

Homework

- Workbook Exercise 52
- Workbook Exercise 53

Notes

The liter is introduced here as a standard unit of capacity. Students should learn how much a liter is and be able to estimate the capacities of various containers in liters. If possible, let them have plenty of practical experience in measuring the capacity of the containers.

You can review other units of measurement at this time. The need for standard units of measurements was discussed in *Primary Mathematics 2A*. Students learned to measure length in meters, and centimeters and to measure weight in kilograms and grams.

Activity 6.2a   **Estimate and measure capacity in liters**

1. Introduce liters as a measurement of capacity
   - Have ready colored water, a liter beaker, paper cups, some containers of less than, more than, and almost 1 liter capacity, a basin and some other containers such as a kettle and a watering can that can hold several liters.
   - Discuss the various standard units of measurement students have already learned for length and weight. Ask students why standard units of measurement are needed.
   - Tell students that there are also standard units of measurement for capacity.
   - Show them a liter beaker or measuring cup. Write "liter" on the board. Tell them *liter* is abbreviated as L or ℓ.
     - Point to the line marked for 1 liter and fill the beaker to 1 liter using the colored water.
     - Tell students that when we fill the container to the line, the amount of water is 1 liter.
   - Have one student come up and do the activity in the **text, p. 72**.
   - Discuss **task 1, text p. 73**.
   - Call on several students to do this task with the containers
   - Discuss **tasks 2-3, text p. 74**.
   - Discuss **task 5, text p. 75**.
   - Call on a student to do the activities in **task 4, text p. 74,** and **task 6, text p. 75**. You can use a liter beaker rather than marking a bottle. Before each student measures the capacity, have him or her first estimate what the capacity will be.
   - You may want to do workbook exercise 52 in class.

Workbook Exercise 52
ᵁˢ Workbook Exercise 53, problems 1-2
³ᵈ Workbook Exercise 53

Activity 6.2b   **Word problems**

1. Discuss **Practice 6A, text p. 76**. Students can solve these individually and then share their solutions.

ᵁˢ Workbook Exercise 53, problems 3-4
³ᵈ Workbook Exercise 54

US Part 3: Gallons, Quarts, Pints and Cups (USpp. 77-80)   2 sessions

Objectives

- Understand the gallon, half-gallon, quart, pint, and cup as units of measurement.
- Estimate and measure the capacity of containers in gallons, quarts, pints, or cups.
- Relate gallons, quarts, pints, and cups to each other.
- Compare quart to liter.

Materials

- A large basin to catch spills
- Colored water
- Liquid measuring set with cup, pint, quart, half-gallon and gallon measuring cups or jars.
- Empty containers of familiar things sold by liquid measurement, e.g., gallon milk jug, quart, pint, and cup milk cartons
- Various containers
- Various other containers of things sold by liquid measurement, e.g. detergent bottles

Homework

- Workbook Exercise 54

Notes

In the US edition, students also learned to measure length in yards, feet, and inches, and to measure weight in pounds and ounces.

In this section, students are introduced to gallons, quarts, cups, and pints as standard units of measurement customarily used in the U.S.

You can use the relationships between these measurements to review multiplication and division by 2 and 4. Conversion of measurements will be covered more fully in *Primary Mathematics 3B*.

Make sure students know that they are learning two different systems of measurement, the metric system and the U.S. customary system. Tell students that the metric system is used in most of the world, and is the measurement system used in science.

Activity 6.3a   **Gallons, quarts, pints, and cups**

1. Introduce measurements for capacity used in the U.S.
   - Tell students that in the U.S. we customarily use other units of measurement than the liter. See if students know what they are. Show students the cup, pint, quart, half-gallon, and gallon measuring cups or jars.
   - Call on students to come up and find out how many cups are in a pint, pints in a quart, quart in a half-gallon, and half-gallons in a gallon.

     | 2 cups = 1 pint |
     | 2 pints = 1 quart |
     | 2 quarts = 1 half-gallon |
     | 2 half-gallons = 1 gallon |

     o Remind them that they fill the measuring cup to the line.
     o Write their results down.
     o Have them copy the results in their journal.
   - Discuss **text pp. 71-72**
   - Call on students to come up and do the activities in the **tasks 1-4, text pp. 78-79**.
     o In these activities they are finding the number of paper cups they can fill with the various measuring containers in order to get a feel for their capacities.
     o Have them estimate the number of paper cups they will fill first.
   - Show students various familiar containers, such as gallon milk jugs, milk cartons, yogurt, or cottage cheese containers.
     o Ask students to estimate the capacities of these containers in cups, pints, quarts, or half-gallons.
     o You can have them come up and test their estimates using the measuring cups.
   - Show students the liter and quart measuring cups. Ask students how they can find out which has a greater capacity. Have them come up and test their ideas to find out which is more, a quart or a liter. A liter is slightly more than a quart. (**NOTE: The first edition of the textbook has this reversed on p. 80. The label for the container with slightly more water should be 1 liter and the one with slightly less water should be 1 quart, and the statement below the picture should read: 1 quart of water is slightly less than 1 liter of water.**)

Activity 6.3b   **Word problems**

1. Discuss **task 5, text p. 80**. Provide some other examples:
   - What unit of measure would you most likely use to measure
     ➢ the amount of water in the bathtub?
     ➢ the amount of gas to put in a car?
     ➢ the amount of juice to make for a party?
     ➢ the amount of milk you put on your cereal?

2. Discuss liquid measurements used in cooking.
   - Sometimes we use half a cup or a fourth a cup in cooking. Show how to use a liquid measuring cup to measure these amounts.
   - You may want to briefly discuss tablespoons and teaspoons. There are 3 teaspoons in a tablespoon and 16 tablespoons in a fourth of a cup. You can use some colored water and the classroom measuring set and call on a student to find the number of tablespoons in a fourth of a cup, for example.

3. Find the number of cups in a quart and quarts in a gallon.
   - Ask your students for the number of cups in a pint, pints in a quart, quarts in a half-gallon, and half-gallons in a gallon. Write the table on the board again.

   | 2 cups = 1 pint |
   | 2 pints = 1 quart |
   | 2 quarts = 1 half-gallon |
   | 2 half-gallons = 1 gallon |

- Ask students to use this information to find the number of cups in a quart and the number of quarts in a gallon. If 2 cups are in a pint, and 2 pints in a quart, then there are 2 x 2 cups in a quart.
- See if they can find the number of cups in a gallon. If 4 cups are in a quart, and 4 quarts in a gallon, then there are 4 x 4 cups in a gallon.
- Use may want to use liquid measurement as an opportunity to practice multiplication and division by 2 and 4. Ask questions such as:
  - ➢ How many cups are in 8 pints?
  - ➢ How many cups are in 5 quarts?
  - ➢ How many quarts are in 6 gallons?
  - ➢ How many cups are in 6 pints?
  - ➢ How many quarts are in 14 pints?
  - ➢ How many gallons are in 12 quarts?
  - ➢ How many pints are in half a quart?
  - ➢ How many cups are in half a quart?

US Workbook Exercise 54

Unit 7 – Graphs

Objectives

• Make, read, and interpret picture graphs with scales.

Suggested number of sessions: 3

Part 1 : Picture Graphs				3 sessions
	Objectives	**Textbook**	**Workbook**	**Activity**
64	• Understand and create picture graphs with scales. • Read and interpret picture graphs with scales.	US pp. 82-84 3d pp. 78-80		7.1a
65		US p. 85, task 1 3d p. 81, task 1	Ex. 55 Ex. 56	7.1b
66		US pp. 86-87, tasks 2-3 3d pp. 82-83, tasks 2-3	Ex. 57 Ex. 58	7.1c

Part 1: Picture Graphs (US pp. 82-87, 3d pp. 78-83)   3 sessions

Objectives

* Make, read, and interpret picture graphs with scales.

Materials

* Counters
* Coins
* Large sheets of paper with columns already drawn
* Cut outs or stickers of squares, triangles, circles, etc.

Homework

* Workbook Exercise 55
* Workbook Exercise 56
* Workbook Exercise 57
* Workbook Exercise 58

Notes

In *Primary Mathematics 1*, students learned to interpret picture graphs where one symbol represented one item being graphed. Here they will learn to create and interpret picture graphs where one symbol represents more than one item. The scale used should be 2, 3, 4, 5, or 10. This will reinforce the multiplication facts learned earlier.

At this stage, students will not be using partial symbols to represent ½ or ¼.

While doing this unit, you can teach your students how to tally. Tallying is used to keep track of counts when it is not easy to remember the last counted number, or when trying to keep track of the number of several things at once, such as when counting car colors or bird species. To tally, one mark is made for each count. Every fifth mark is drawn across the previous four. The total can be found by counting by fives or tens.

Activity 7.1a   **Picture graphs**

1. Review picture graphs where each symbol represents one item and introduces scaled picture graphs.
   - Discuss **text** [US]**pp. 82-83** ([3d]**pp. 78-79**). Students should count the fruits and the symbols on the graph to see that they are the same.
   - Discuss **text** [US]**p. 84** ([3d]**p. 80**). This is a graph of the same data, but here each symbol stands for two fruit.
     - o Point out that in both graphs, the shapes are lined up and in even rows across. This makes it easier to see when there are more or less of each thing.

2. Guide students in tallying data and creating a picture graph with a scale of 1 to 2.
   - List four or five fruits or other items (seasons of the year, colors, or other foods).
     - o Have students tell you their favorite. As they tell you, make a mark next to their choice. The fifth mark crosses the previous four marks. When you are done tallying their choices, explain what you did. Point out that it is easy to count up the total for each choice by counting by fives.
     - o Provide students with large sheets of paper and cutout shapes, stickers, or counters. Have them make a picture graph based on a scale of 1 to 1.
     - o Discuss the graphs. Ask questions such as "How many liked oranges best" or "How many more liked apples than bananas?"
   - Have students make a graph of the same data (or collect other data, or just provide them with data) using a scale of 1 to 2. You may have to adjust the data so that the values are even to avoid half-symbols. Tell students they need to indicate the scale on their graphs. Discuss these graphs.

Activity 7.1b   **Scaled picture graphs**

1. Discuss **task 1, text** [US]**p. 85** ([3d]**p. 81**).

2. Guide students in tallying data and creating a picture graph with a scale of 1 to 3 or 4..
   - Divide students into groups and give each group coins (pennies, nickels, dimes and quarters) or counters of 4 different colors, several papers with columns drawn on them, and some stickers or cutouts. Prepare the amount of items ahead of time so that the quantity of each item is a multiple of 3 or 4.
   - Each group should count their items and create a graph according to type (coins) or color. They should choose a scale of either 3 or 4.
   - Have a representative of each group present their data. The other group members can come up with questions to ask the rest of the class based on the data.

Workbook Exercises 55-56

Activity 7.1c   **More picture graphs**

1. Provide more practice in interpreting scaled picture graphs.
   - Draw some pictures or use objects and ask questions such as the following, using only multiples of 2, 3, 4, 5, or 10.

     ➢ If ♥ stands for 4 objects, then ♥♥♥♥ stand for _____ objects.

     ➢ If $ stands for $3, then $27 is shown with _____ $'s.

     ➢ If 🌲🌲🌲🌲🌲 stands for 25 trees, then one 🌲 stands for _____ trees.

     ➢ If ☆☆☆☆☆☆ represents 60, then 90 can be shown by _____ ☆'s.

   - Discuss **tasks 2-3, text** US**pp. 86-87 (**3d**pp. 82-83)**

2. Provide students with some data to graph and have the students complete the graph. Use multiples of 2, 3, 4, or 5 for the data. An example is given on the next page of this guide. In this example the graph is a horizontal one.
   - Allow the students to choose the scale, the symbol they will use, and the order in which to put their data. Point out that graphs should have titles, and the scale should always be given.
   - Ask questions about the completed graph.

Complete the graph below to show how much money each student has.

Jerry has $24.
Mike has $12.
Paula has $15.
Mary has $30.
Peter has $18.

Amount of Money	
Each _____ stands for _____	

Review

Objectives

• Review all topics.

Suggested number of sessions: 2

	Objectives	Textbook	Workbook	Activity
67	▪ Review	Review E, ^{US}p. 81, ^{3d}p. 77		R.4
68		Review F, ^{US}p. 88, ^{3d}p. 84 Review G, ^{US}p. 89, ^{3d}p. 85		

Activity R.4   **Review**

1. Use **text Reviews E, F, and G** to review concepts learned so far.

2. Provide additional review as necessary. You can use Mental Math worksheets and games from previous units.

Unit 8 – Geometry

Objectives

- Identify and name common shapes on 3-dimensional objects.
- Identify flat and curved faces on 3-dimensional objects.
- Combine common shapes to make a new 2-dimensional shape.
- Identify common shapes within a 2-dimensional shape.
- Identify straight and curved lines.
- Describe and continue a pattern according to 1 or 2 attributes.

Suggested number of sessions: 5

	Objectives	Textbook	Workbook	Activity
Part 1 : Flat and Curved Faces				**2 sessions**
69	• Identify and basic shapes on 3-dimensional objects. • Combine shapes into a common shape	US pp. 90-91 3d pp. 86-87	Ex. 59,#1-3	8.1a
70	• Identify flat and curved faces on 3-dimensional objects.	US p. 92, task 1 3d p. 88, task 1	Ex. 59, #4	8.1b
Part 2 : Making Shapes				**3 sessions**
71	• Make composite figures from basic shapes. • Identify straight and curved lines.	US p. 93 US p. 94, task 1 3d p. 89 38 p. 90, task 1	Ex. 61	8.2a
	• Make shapes with straight and curved lines.	US p. 97, task 5 3d p. 93, task 5	Ex. 63	
72	• Identify half circles and quarter circles. • Fit basic shapes together to make new shapes. • Divide a shape into common shapes.	US pp. 95-97, tasks 2-4 3d pp. 91-93, tasks 2-4	Ex. 60 Ex. 62	8.2b
73	• Describe and continue a pattern according to 1 or 2 attributes of color, shape, size, or orientation.	US pp. 98-99, tasks 6-7 3d pp. 94-95, tasks 6-7	Ex. 44	8.2c

Part 1: Flat and Curved Faces (USpp. 90-92, 3dpp. 86-88)   **2 sessions**

Objectives

- Identify rectangles, circles, squares, and triangles on 3-dimensional objects.
- Identify flat and curved faces on 3-dimensional objects.
- Find combinations that make a familiar shape.

Materials

- Models of cubes, cuboids (rectangular prism), cylinders, cones, and triangular prisms
- Objects in the shapes of cubes, cuboids, cylinders
- Cloth to use as blindfold, one per group
- Large paper shapes of rectangles, squares, circles, and triangles

Homework

- Workbook Exercise 59
- Workbook Exercise 60

Notes

In Primary Mathematics 1, students learned to identify the four basic shapes — squares, rectangles, circles, and triangles, and to combine these shapes into new shapes. Here, they will learn to recognize these shapes on three dimensional objects and distinguish between flat and curved surfaces.

The shapes used in the text are primarily cubes, cuboids (rectangular prisms), cylinders, cones, and triangular prisms.

In this curriculum, rectangular prisms are given the name of cuboid. Students are not required to learn the names for the 3-dimensional objects. They may use familiar names — such as box, can, or cone — but they do not need to identify the 3-dimensional shapes by name yet.

cuboid or
rectangular prism

triangular prism

Students should handle real objects or 3-dimensional models which contain the four basic shapes.

Activity 8.1a   **Common 3-D objects**

1. Review two dimensional shapes.
   - Draw some shapes of squares, rectangles, circles, and triangles on the board and ask students for their names and distinguishing characteristics. Write the names on the board. Have students draw the shapes and write their names in their journals.

2. Introduce three dimensional shapes.
   - Show students some 3-dimensional objects that have similar shapes, such as a two different boxes or a can and another item that has a cylindrical shape. Ask students if they can see and name a shape on the surface of the items.
   - Discuss **text** ^US^**pp. 90-91** (^3d^**pp. 86-87**). Ask students what shapes led to the pairings shown on p. 91.
   - Name a shape and have students look around the classroom to see if they can find an object that has that shape.

3. Provide students with opportunities to physically explore the 3-dimensional shapes.
   - Divide students into groups and provide them with some 3-dimensional shapes. Try to have at least two different shapes that are similar for each group, and some with each of the four basic shapes on one surface.
     o Ask students to group or pair similar shapes and then have a representative from the group explain why they paired the shapes as they did.
     o Have students place a flat surface down on paper, and trace around the shape, and name the shape.
     o Students can cut out their shapes, cut each shape into 2-4 pieces using straight cuts. and pass their cut pieces to another student, who tries to reassemble the shape.

Workbook Exercise 59, problems 1-3

Activity 8.1b   **Curved and flat surfaces**

1. Illustrate curved and flat surfaces.
   - Show students a variety of 3-dimensional shapes. Call on students to show you the curved or flat surfaces on their shapes. Ask them to tell you how many of the surfaces are curved and how many are flat.
   - Discuss **task 1, text** ^US^**p. 92** (^3d^**p. 88**). Use similar 3-D objects and relate them to the pictures on the page.

2. Provide students with opportunities to physically explore curved and flat surfaces.
   - Divide students up into groups. Provide each group with a variety of 3-dimensional objects.
     o Students take turns being blindfolded and trying to tell how many flat and curved faces there are on one of the objects.

Workbook Exercise 59, problem 4

Part 2: Making Shapes (^{US}pp. 93-99, ^{3d}pp. 89-95)   **3 sessions**

Objectives

- Combine common shapes to make new shapes.
- Identify half circles and quarter circles.
- Divide a shape into common shapes.
- Identify straight and curved lines.
- Make shapes with straight and curved lines.
- Describe and continue a pattern according to 1 or 2 attributes of color, shape, size, or orientation.

Materials

- Colored paper shapes that will fit together (the side on one shape is equal to a side on another, see activity 8.2a)
- Paper circles
- Connect-a-cubes
- Geo-shapes

Homework

- Workbook Exercise 61
- Workbook Exercise 62
- Workbook Exercise 63
- Workbook Exercise 64

Notes

Students formed compound figures in *Primary Mathematics 1*. This is extended here to include half circles and quarter circles. Students should be able to identify basic shapes in composite figures. Students will also identify straight lines and curves which form a given 2-dimensional figure, and to draw figures with a specified number of straight lines and curves.

In *Primary Mathematics 1*, students learned to recognize and continue patterns based on one or two attributes — size, shape, or color. In this section they will also look for patterns based on orientation.

If time permits, you can supplement this unit with activities involving tangrams or pattern blocks. They can form patterns and shapes with the pattern blocks and tangrams.
They can form and describe patterns using attribute blocks based on size, shape, color, orientation, or thickness.

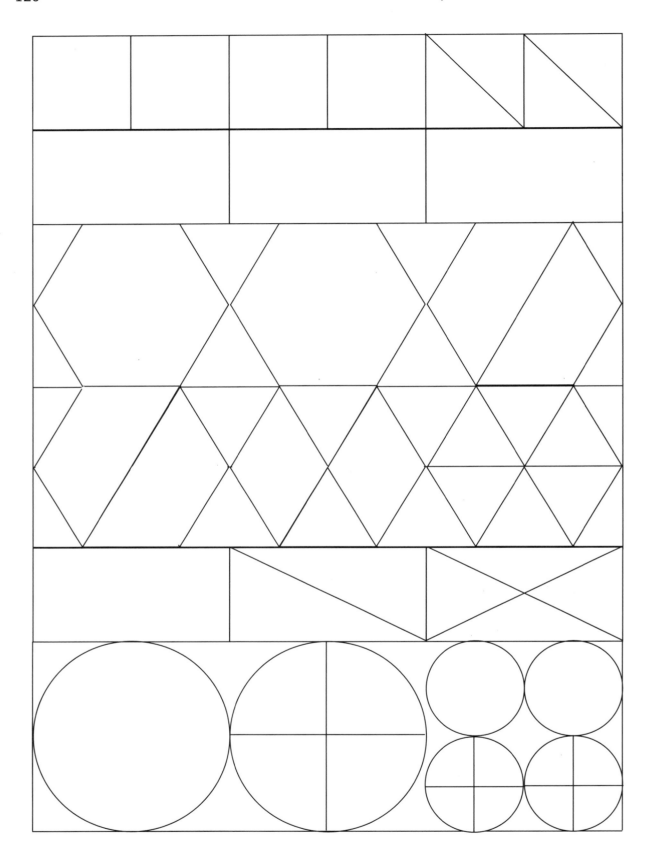

Tangrams

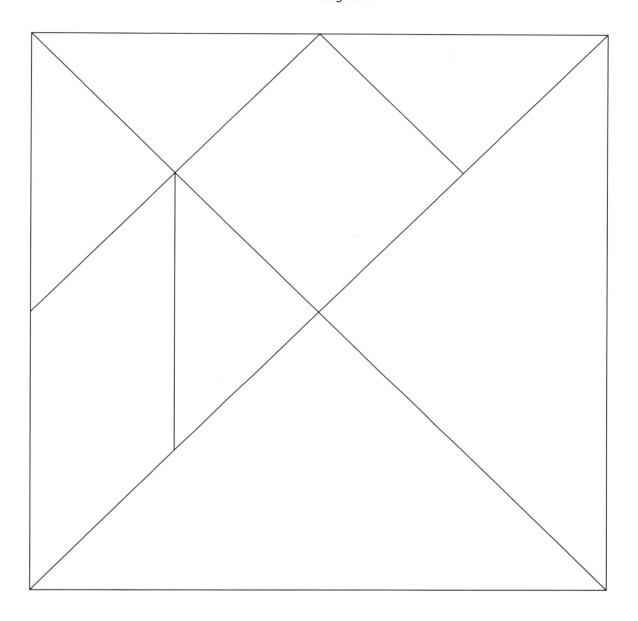

Activity 8.2a   **Composite figures**

1. Discuss and have students create composite figures.
   - Provide students with paper shapes. Stickers in shapes that fit together would be ideal if you have that available. Or, you can copy p. 120 of this guide onto colored paper and cut out the shapes. Do not use the circles yet.
   - Discuss text and have students do activities in the **text** ^{US}**p. 93** (^{3d}**p. 89**) and **task 1, text** ^{US}**p. 94,** (^{3d}**p. 90**).
   - Have students make other shapes and paste them onto paper. You can tell them to use a specified number of certain shapes and then have the students compare their figures. They should talk about the shapes they have made.

2. Discuss straight and curved lines.
   - Discuss **task 5, text** ^{US}**p. 97** (^{3d}**p. 93**).
   - Have students talk about the number of straight and curved lines in the figures they made earlier.

3. Optional: Give students the paper tangrams (copy the page following the next page).
   - Have them cut the pieces apart, mix them up, then try to put them back together to form the square.
   - They can make other shapes from them as well.

Workbook Exercise 61 and 63

Activity 8.2b   **Half and quarter circles**

1. Discuss half and quarter circles and have students create composite figures.
   - Provide students with paper circles. Have them do the activity in the **task 2, text** ^{US}**p. 95** (^{3d}**p. 91**).
   - Provide students with paper shapes including circles, half circles, and quarter circles. Have them make composite shapes and paste them onto paper. You can tell them to use a specified number of specific shapes. Then have the trace their shapes using a paper laid over their pasted shapes. Have student pair up and see if they can divide their partner's shapes into the original basic shapes.
   - Discuss **tasks 3-4, text** ^{US}**pp. 96-97** (^{3d}**pp. 92-93**).

Workbook Exercises 60 and 62

Activity 8.2c   **Patterns**

1. Discuss **tasks 6-7, text** ^{US}**pp. 98-99** (^{3d}**pp. 94-95**).
   - Students should determine what attribute(s) change in the pattern — color, shape, size, or orientation — and what the next figure should look like.
   - Verbalizing these attributes may help students see the pattern. For example, in 6(a) the student can say "circle, triangle, circle, square, circle, triangle" and from this determine that a circle comes next.
   - If two attributes change, they can concentrate on one at a time. For example, in 7(c) the shape and the orientation change. The student can first say "rectangle, triangle, triangle, rectangle, triangle, triangle" to see that a rectangle comes next. Then they can concentrate on the orientation of the rectangle.

2. Provide practice in creating patterns.
   - Divide students into groups. Provide each group with connect-a-cubes and geo shapes, or paper shapes.
   - Students create patterns that vary by only two attributes at most. Other students try to continue the pattern.

Workbook Exercise 64

Review

Objectives

- Review all topics.

Suggested number of sessions: 1

	Objectives	Textbook	Workbook	Activity
74	▪ Review.	US pp. 100-101, Review H 3d pp. 96-97, Review H	Review 6	R.5

Activity R.5   **Review**

1. Use **text Review H** to review concepts learned so far.

2. Include some review of fractions.

Workbook Review 6

Unit 9 – Area

Objectives

- Understand the concept of area.
- Measure in nonstandard square units.
- Compare areas in square units and half squares.

Suggested number of sessions: 3

	Objectives	Textbook	Workbook	Activity
Unit 9 Part 1 : Square Units				**3 sessions**
75	• Understand the concept of area. • Understand the term square unit. • Recognize that different figures can have the same area.	US p. 102 US pp. 103-104, tasks 1-3 3d p. 98 3d pp. 99-100, tasks 1-3	Ex. 65	9.1a
76	• Determine and compare areas in square units and half-squares.	US p. 105, tasks 4-5 3d p. 101, tasks 4-5	Ex. 66 Ex. 67	9.1b
77	• (Optional) Determine area of irregular figures			9.1c

Part 1: Square Units (^{US}pp. 102-105, ^{3d}pp. 98-101)   **3 sessions**

Objectives
- Understand the concept of area.
- Measure in nonstandard square units.
- Compare areas in square units and half squares.

Materials
- Paper squares and half-squares, or tiles
- Square graph paper

Homework
- Workbook Exercise 65
- Workbook Exercise 66
- Workbook Exercise 67

Notes

The area of a figure is the amount of 2-dimensional (flat) space covered by a figure. It is measured in square units. Students will be measuring and comparing areas in nonstandard square units. The final areas will include only whole or half units at this stage.

Activity 9.1a   **Area**

1. Introduce the concept of area and square units.
   - Tell students that area is the amount of space covered. Discuss the term in everyday use that students might be familiar with, for example, area rugs, area of a room, acres of land, etc.
   - Discuss **text ^{US}p. 102 (^{3d}p. 98)**.
   - Provide students with square graph paper. Have them outline and shade a figure on it. Their shapes should have only whole or half squares. Then have them write the area as _____ square units.
   - Discuss **tasks 1-2, text ^{US}pp. 103-104 (^{3d}pp. 99-100)**. Provide students with square paper shapes so they can do task 2. You can copy the squares on p. 127 of this guide onto cardstock or cut squares out of index cards.
   - Draw a figure on the board in squares and half squares. Have students make a figure of the same area but a different shape. Have them copy their figures onto square graph paper. The squares on the graph paper should be the same size as the squares they are arranging.
   - Repeat with figures of other areas. Leave each figure on the board. After several figures, label them and ask students to order them by size.

Workbook Exercise 65

Activity 9.1b   **Square units**

1. Have students find the area of figures.
   - Provide students with square paper shapes.
     - o Draw two squares on the board.
     - o Ask students to put two of their squares together and draw a line through both of them as shown, color one of the two resulting triangles, and then cut each shape apart (there will be 4 shapes). Have them put the shaded shapes together to form a square.
     - o They should see that the area of the two pieces together make one whole square.
   - Discuss **tasks 4-5, text ^{US}p. 105 (^{3d}p. 101)**.

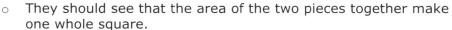

2. Provide additional practice.
   - Divide students into groups. Provide them with paper squares.
     - o Ask students to find out how many different shapes can be formed from 5 whole squares. Each student has to make a different shape.
     - o Have students form shapes that have a specified area. They can cut their squares into half squares or cut two squares together into half, as in the previous activity. Students compare their shapes. Each figure should be different. They can paste the figures in their journals and write down the areas in square units.
     - o Have students create shapes within a range of areas, such as between 8 and 12 square units. Students then determine if any of them have shapes of the same size. Students can draw models of the shapes on centimeter graph paper.

Workbook Exercises 66-67

Activity 9.1c (optional)   **Area of irregular figures**

1. Discuss finding the area of irregular figures.
   • Draw some other squares on the board and draw an irregular curved shape through them. Shade one part.

     o Ask students whether the shaded part is more or less than one half of a square. Tell them two figures, one more than half a square, and less than half a square, can be counted together to have an area of *about* 1 square.
     o Draw an irregular shape on square centimeter paper and shade it. Have students count the whole squares and write the total down. Have student pair and mark off squares that are less than half shaded with squares that are more than half shaded. You can tally the number of almost 1 square unit. Then have the students give you the total area of the figure as almost _____ square units.

   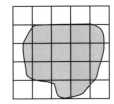

   Area is about 13 and a half square units.

   • Provide students with centimeter graph paper. Have them trace their hands and find the area of their hand prints. They can compare the areas of their hands.

Review

Objectives

- Review all topics.

Suggested number of sessions: 3

	Objectives	Textbook	Workbook	Activity
78		US pp. 106-108, Review I		
79	▪ Review	US pp. 109-112, Review J	Review 7	R.6
		3d pp. 102-104, Review I	Review 8	
80				

Activity R.6   **Review**

1. US: Use **text Reviews I and J** to review concepts.
   3d: Use **text Review I** to review concepts.

2. Provide additional review as necessary.

3. Have students play favorite games or do other practice, particularly fact practice for multiplication and division by 2, 3, 4, 5 and 10

Workbook Review 7
Workbook Review 8

Mental Math Worksheets Answer Key

	Mental Math 1				Mental Math 2				Mental Math 3		
1.	80	16.	68	1.	25	16.	65	1.	27	16.	89
2.	25	17.	29	2.	70	17.	75	2.	67	17.	67
3.	93	18.	43	3.	35	18.	60	3.	50	18.	41
4.	2	19.	40	4.	77	19.	94	4.	65	19.	86
5.	94	20.	60	5.	15	20.	90	5.	33	20.	30
6.	65	21.	65	6.	20	21.	85	6.	29	21.	24
7.	52	22.	97	7.	52	22.	38	7.	72	22.	27
8.	75	23.	78	8.	78	23.	64	8.	81	23.	77
9.	54	24.	50	9.	92	24.	75	9.	78	24.	20
10.	90	25.	39	10.	81	25.	19	10.	42	25.	68
11.	23	26.	16	11.	36	26.	100	11.	35	26.	39
12.	88	27.	47	12.	9	27.	194	12.	38	27.	62
13.	95	28.	62	13.	56	28.	121	13.	60	28.	18
14.	71	29.	21	14.	26	29.	34	14.	28	29.	91
15.	67	30.	91	15.	69	30.	25	15.	32	30.	100

	Mental Math 4				Mental Math 5				Mental Math 6		
1.	91	16.	77	1.	417	16.	623	1.	494	16.	735
2.	82	17.	120	2.	630	17.	873	2.	768	17.	938
3.	98	18.	110	3.	328	18.	864	3.	520	18.	657
4.	52	19.	45	4.	912	19.	160	4.	382	19.	211
5.	118	20.	136	5.	816	20.	497	5.	697	20.	449
6.	62	21.	127	6.	310	21.	813	6.	341	21.	670
7.	124	22.	122	7.	113	22.	225	7.	591	22.	572
8.	126	23.	83	8.	720	23.	630	8.	289	23.	869
9.	72	24.	150	9.	850	24.	254	9.	420	24.	981
10.	102	25.	150	10.	391	25.	883	10.	512	25.	952
11.	137	26.	92	11.	154	26.	210	11.	947	26.	871
12.	72	27.	100	12.	262	27.	323	12.	325	27.	558
13.	160	28.	108	13.	787	28.	130	13.	464	28.	967
14.	98	29.	84	14.	395	29.	183	14.	660	29.	556
15.	78	30.	104	15.	110	30.	400	15.	239	30.	1073

Mental Math 7

1.	113	16.	515
2.	133	17.	432
3.	104	18.	366
4.	131	19.	336
5.	146	20.	604
6.	123	21.	680
7.	150	22.	280
8.	169	23.	423
9.	171	24.	689
10.	113	25.	501
11.	196	26.	132
12.	624	27.	309
13.	415	28.	224
14.	739	29.	393
15.	911	30.	727

Mental Math 8

1.	82	16.	35
2.	36	17.	65
3.	15	18.	24
4.	86	19.	78
5.	78	20.	58
6.	29	21.	55
7.	56	22.	47
8.	68	23.	47
9.	44	24.	24
10.	87	25.	79
11.	29	26.	46
12.	23	27.	29
13.	36	28.	73
14.	67	29.	37
15.	69	30.	49

Mental Math 9

1.	182	16.	35
2.	626	17.	874
3.	115	18.	384
4.	866	19.	818
5.	818	20.	637
6.	419	21.	705
7.	746	22.	447
8.	358	23.	947
9.	742	24.	814
10.	467	25.	657
11.	239	26.	416
12.	573	27.	324
13.	546	28.	263
14.	167	29.	412
15.	658	30.	200

Mental Math 10

1.	268	16.	460
2.	821	17.	150
3.	601	18.	330
4.	358	19.	640
5.	262	20.	460
6.	560	21.	580
7.	730	22.	62
8.	160	23.	477
9.	660	24.	420
10.	130	25.	730
11.	550	26.	133
12.	870	27.	232
13.	420	28.	516
14.	340	29.	42
15.	190	30.	190

Mental Math 11

1.	102	16.	266
2.	301	17.	687
3.	401	18.	157
4.	501	19.	160
5.	3	20.	664
6.	601	21.	366
7.	261	22.	159
8.	732	23.	105
9.	712	24.	461
10.	621	25.	603
11.	333	26.	586
12.	500	27.	688
13.	644	28.	665
14.	153	29.	115
15.	334	30.	82

Mental Math 13

1.	7	16.	3
2.	4	17.	1
3.	2	18.	9
4.	4	19.	6
5.	5	20.	5
6.	6	21.	8
7.	9	22.	6
8.	7	23.	10
9.	7	24.	5
10.	2	25.	3
11.	9	26.	8
12.	8	27.	1
13.	10	28.	4
14.	3	29.	9
15.	10	30.	6

Mental Math 12

x	6	4	7	3	9	8	1	2	10	5
2	12	8	14	6	18	16	2	4	20	10
3	18	12	21	9	27	24	3	6	30	15
4	24	16	28	12	36	32	4	8	40	20

x	2	8	3	6	1	9	5	4	7	10
4	8	32	12	24	4	36	20	16	28	40
2	4	16	6	12	2	18	10	8	14	20
3	6	24	9	18	3	27	15	12	21	30

x	10	1	4	5	2	7	3	8	9	6
3	30	3	12	15	6	21	9	24	27	18
4	40	4	16	20	8	28	12	32	36	24
2	20	2	8	10	4	14	6	16	18	12

Mental Math 14

x	6	4	3	5	10	2	1	8	9	7
3	18	12	9	15	30	6	3	24	27	21
4	24	16	12	20	40	8	4	32	36	28
5	30	20	15	25	50	10	5	40	45	35

x	3	2	6	8	1	10	9	7	5	4
5	15	10	30	40	5	50	45	35	25	20
3	9	6	18	24	3	30	27	21	15	12
4	12	8	24	32	4	40	36	28	20	16

x	7	1	4	2	3	5	8	6	9	10
2	14	2	8	4	6	10	16	12	18	20
5	35	5	20	10	15	25	40	30	45	50
3	21	3	12	6	9	15	24	18	27	30

Mental Math 15		Mental Math 16		Mental Math 17	
1. 5	16. 9	1. 27	16. 77	1. 32	16. 7
2. 6	17. 10	2. 220	17. 583	2. 36	17. 28
3. 4	18. 8	3. 58	18. 127	3. 40	18. 35
4. 7	19. 2	4. 95	19. 292	4. 8	19. 4
5. 9	20. 6	5. 700	20. 930	5. 5	20. 40
6. 4	21. 3	6. 123	21. 65	6. 20	21. 6
7. 2	22. 6	7. 430	22. 53	7. 8	22. 45
8. 7	23. 5	8. 789	23. 305	8. 16	23. 6
9. 3	24. 4	9. 382	24. 784	9. 5	24. 25
10. 5	25. 5	10. 297	25. 19	10. 30	25. 9
11. 1	26. 9	11. 369	26. 489	11. 32	26. 4
12. 5	27. 7	12. 516	27. 211	12. 9	27. 8
13. 9	28. 7	13. 533	28. 425	13. 7	28. 24
14. 9	29. 6	14. 560	29. 75	14. 50	29. 2
15. 8	30. 10	15. 822	30. 752	15. 15	30. 3

Mental Math 18		Mental Math 19		Mental Math 20	
1. 60	16. 8	1. 35	16. 7.34	1. 4.30	16. 1.39
2. 100	17. 80	2. 25	17. 6.32	2. 2.15	17. 5.08
3. 28	18. 5	3. 6.25	18. 3.12	3. 4.66	18. 1.99
4. 4	19. 18	4. 1.85	19. 9.02	4. 0.25	19. 4.73
5. 12	20. 9	5. 59	20. 7.23	5. 5.55	20. 5.85
6. 35	21. 6	6. 7	21. 7.92	6. 7.77	21. 5.88
7. 6	22. 7	7. 4.92	22. 4.04	7. 9.35	22. 2.88
8. 20	23. 9	8. 7.30	23. 754	8. 6.90	23. 3.01
9. 3	24. 8	9. 8.65	24. 5.00	9. 3.55	24. 34
10. 90	25. 10	10. 9.32	25. 6.50	10. 4.55	25. 70
11. 4	26. 10	11. 6.75	26. 5.85	11. 4.62	26. 54
12. 9	27. 4	12. 3.83	27. 6.25	12. 3.45	27. 7.30
13. 7	28. 8	13. 9.00	28. 0.35	13. 4.91	28. 7.35
14. 25	29. 3	14. 8.75	29. 1.35	14. 3.60	29. 7.40
15. 45	30. 6	15. 4.38	30. 9.35	15. 2.24	30. 7.70

Textbook Answer Key

Unit 1 - Addition and Subtraction

Part1: Finding the Missing Number (pp. 6-10)

5
1. 8
2. (a) 16   (b) 16   (c) 24
3. (a) 9   (b) 7
   (c) 30   (d) 28
   (e) 7   (f) 17
   (g) 46   (h) 56
5. 47
6. (a) 66   (b) 24
   (c) 18   (d) 91
7. (a) 74   (b) 39   (c) 58
   (d) 4   (e) 98   (f) 92

Practice 1A (p. 11)

1. (a) 15   (b) 17   (c) 39
   (d) 22   (e) 14   (f) 90
   (g) 54   (h) 72   (i) 75
   (j) 7   (k) 37   (l) 43
2. (a) 62   (b) 1   (c) 2
   (d) 96   (e) 91   (f) 97
3. 179
4. $180
5. (a) 238 g   (b) 562 g

Part 2: Methods for Mental Addition (pp. 12-14)

358, 556
1. (a) 49   (b) 45   (c) 61
   (d) 50   (e) 90   (f) 140
   (g) 54   (h) 93   (i) 147
2. (a) 162   (b) 283   (c) 612
   (d) 380   (e) 305   (f) 214
   (g) 400   (h) 800   (i) 900
   (j) 456   (k) 804   (l) 965
3. 69
4. (a) 69   (b) 77   (c) 88
   (d) 79   (e) 79   (f) 59
5. 103
6. (a) 101   (b) 108   (c) 103
   (d) 145   (e) 157   (f) 134
7. (a) 127   (b) 153   (c) 194
   (d) 155   (e) 184   (f) 197
8. 336
9. (a) 355   (b) 406   (c) 751
   (d) 202   (e) 561   (f) 397

Part 3: Methods for Mental Subtraction (pp. 15-17)

574, 178
1. (a) 36   (b) 18   (c) 61
   (d) 20   (e) 50   (f) 40
   (g) 21   (h) 58   (i) 45
2. (a) 223   (b) 197   (c) 403
   (d) 720   (e) 380   (f) 460
   (g) 300   (h) 300   (i) 600
   (j) 342   (k) 353   (l) 608
3. 31
4. (a) 41   (b) 71   (c) 30
   (d) 11   (e) 23   (f) 20
5. 201
6. (a) 101   (b) 301   (c) 801
   (d) 602   (e) 402   (f) 702
7. 105
8. (a) 3   (b) 209   (c) 506
   (d) 206   (e) 303   (f) 608
9. (a) 141   (b) 247   (c) 613
   (d) 223   (e) 456   (f) 832

Practice 1B (p. 18)

1. (a) 242   (b) 445   (c) 905
2. (a) 89   (b) 161   (c) 402
3. (a) 98   (b) 212   (c) 340
4. (a) 41   (b) 42   (c) 62
5. (a) 226   (b) 308   (c) 501
6. 35
7. 213
8. $402
9. $49
10. (a) 500   (b) 70

Practice 1C (p. 19)

1. (a) 386   (b) 327   (c) 210
2. (a) 250   (b) 411   (c) 500
3. (a) 507   (b) 230   (c) 498
4. (a) 731   (b) 455   (c) 178
5. (a) 202   (b) 359   (c) 502
6. (a) 304   (b) 399
7. 300
8. 164
9. (a) 184   (b) 144
10. (a) 140 kg (b) 60 kg

Unit 2 - Multiplication and Division
Part 1: Multiplying and Dividing by 4 (pp. 20-24)

    12, 28
1. (a) 16   (b) 36
2. 32
3. 20; 28, 28; 36, 36
4. 12, 16, 20, 24, 28, 32, 36, 40
    8, 12, 16, 20, 24, 28, 32, 36, 40
5. 24
6. (a) 3, 3   (b) 3, 3, 3
7. 2; 5, 5; 8; 7, 7
8. (a) 1   (b) 4   (c) 8
   (d) 6   (e) 3   (f) 10
9. (a) 8, 8   (b) 10, 10

Practice 2A (p. 25)

1. (a) 12   (b) 28   (c) 8
2. (a) 1   (b) 8   (c) 4
3. (a) 24   (b) 40   (c) 32
4. (a) 2   (b) 5   (c) 10
5. (a) 9   (b) 3   (c) 6
6. 20
7. 4 kg
8. 24
9. $10
10. 32 m
11. 9

Part 2: Multiplying and Dividing by 5 (pp. 26-28)

1. (a) 15,15   (b) 40, 40
2. 45, 45
3. (a) 30¢   (b) $35
4. 20; 45, 45
5. (a) 35   (b) 30   (c) 5
   (d) 25   (e) 10   (f) 50
6. 3; 8, 8
7. (a) 6   (b) 1   (c) 5
   (d) 2   (e) 10   (f) 9

Practice 2B (p. 29)

1. (a) 25   (b) 20   (c) 35
2. (a) 3   (b) 5   (c) 1
3. (a) 5   (b) 45   (c) 15
4. (a) 4   (b) 6   (c) 9
5. (a) 8   (b) 10   (c) 7
6. $40
7. $35
8. $9
9. 5

10. $15
11. $6

Part 3: Multiplying and Dividing by 10 (pp. 30-31)

1. (a) 40, 40   (b) 60, 60
2. (a) 70¢   (b) $80
3. 40, 40; 70, 70
4. (a) 30   (b) 100   (c) 90
   (d) 20   (e) 10   (f) 60
5. 5; 8, 8
6. (a) 6   (b) 3   (c) 1
   (d) 4   (e) 10   (f) 9

Practice 2C (p. 32)

1. (a) 40   (b) 10   (c) 70
2. (a) 6   (b) 2   (c) 7
3. (a) 60   (b) 50   (c) 100
4. (a) 3   (b) 1   (c) 9
5. (a) 10   (b) 8   (c) 5
6. $70
7. 4
8. $30
9. $8
10. 50 kg
11. 6

Practice 2D (p. 33)

1. (a) 24   (b) 20   (c) 30
2. (a) 3   (b) 4   (c) 4
3. (a) 32   (b) 25   (c) 36
4. (a) 8   (b) 7   (c) 7
5. (a) 45   (b) 30   (c) 80
6. $9
7. 15 m
8. 5
9. 6
10. 8
11. 32

Practice 2E (p. 34)

1. (a) 12   (b) 40   (c) 90
2. (a) 5   (b) 5   (c) 5
3. (a) 36   (b) 70   (c) 16
4. (a) 6   (b) 8   (c) 1
5. (a) 100   (b) 28   (c) 15
6. 5
7. 10
8. 60
9. 10 kg
10. 9
11. $8

Review A (p. 35)

1. (a) 800   (b) 648   (c) 902
2. (a) 260   (b) 9   (c) 401
3. (a) 12   (b) 30   (c) 70
4. (a) 10   (b) 6   (c) 9
5. 42
6. 200
7. 7
8. (a) 5   (b) $45
9. (a) $403   (b) $891

Unit 3 - Money

Part 1: Dollars and cents (pp. 36-40)

1. (a) $23.30   (b) $4.32
   (c) $8   (d) $0.65
3. (a) 4 dollars, 75 cents
   (b) 8 dollars, 0 cents
   (c) 0 dollars, 35 cents
4. (a) 100   (b) 10   (c) 20
5. (a) 1.50   (b) ^{US} 1.50 ^{3d} *1.40*
6. (a) ^{US} 2 ^{3d} *4*
   (b) ^{US} 4 ^{3d} *10*
7. ^{US} $23 ^{3d} *$31*
8. (a) $0.65   (b) $1.65
9. (a) 85¢   (b) 120¢
   (c) 200¢   (d) 205¢
10. 55¢
11. (a) 40¢   (b) 15¢
    (c) 90¢   (d) 95¢
12. (a) 80¢   (b) 25¢
13. (a) $5.70   (b) $7.35
14. (a) $4.60   (b) $3.05

Practice 3A (p. 41)

1. (a) 3 dollars, 45 cents
   (b) 6 dollars, 0 cents
   (c) 7 dollars, 5 cents
   (d) 0 dollars, 80 cents
2. (a) 220¢   (b) 305¢
3. $0.75   (b) $2.60
4. (a) ^{US} 4 ^{3d} *10*
   (b) 4   (c) 5
5. 15¢
6. $1.40

Part 2: Adding Money (pp. 42-45)

   $7.65
1. (a) $6.95   (b) $14.45
2. (a) 75¢   (b) $2.75   (c) $5.75
3. (a) $1   (b) $3   (c) $4
   (d) $1   (e) $2   (f) $4

4. (a) $6.75, $6.95, $6.95
   (b) $8.65, $8.80, $8.80
5. (a) $9.80   (b) $9.75
   (c) $9.90   (d) $7.80
6. (a) $4.25   (b) $7.55
   (c) $7.50   (d) $8.45
7. (a) $7.25, $7.20, $7.20
   (b) $6.60, $6.59, $6.59
8. (a) $4.35   (b) $7.60
   (c) $6.14   (d) $6.24
9. $7.55, $7.55
10. $9.50, $9.50

Part 3: Subtracting Money (pp. 46-49)

   $5.25
1. (a) $5.15   (b) $4.35   (c) $0.80
   (d) $0.45   (e) $2.45   (f) $3.45
2. (a) 60¢   (b) $2.60   (c) $9.60
3. (a) $0.10   (b) $3.40   (c) $5.50
   (d) $1.25   (e) $5.55   (f) $6.95
4. (a) $3.90. $3.40, $3.40
   (b) $1.65, $1.60, $1.60
5. (a) $6.20   (b) $3.55
   (c) $0.40   (d) $4.15
6. (a) $4.80   (b) $3.65   (c) $2.65
   (d) $4.30   (e) $1.60   (f) $1.65
7. (a) $3.60, $3.65, $3.65
   (b) $3.25, $3.26, $3.26
8. (a) $2.50   (b) $2.35
   (c) $3.21   (d) $1.01
9. $1.55, $1.55
10. $3.45, $3.45

Practice 3B (p. 50)

1. (a) $6   (b) $0.35
2. (a) $5.95   (b) $4.05
3. (a) $9.05   (b) $1.80
4. (a) $9.45   (b) $1.55
5. (a) $8.59   (b) $3.15
6. $9.25
7. $3.70
8. $3.15
9. $6.20
10. $7.35

Practice 3C (p. 51)

1. (a) $10   (b) $0.35
2. (a) $9.35   (b) $1.90
3. (a) $9.55   (b) $1.30
4. (a) $10. 20 (b) $1.65
5. (a) $9.75   (a) $0.06

6. $9.20
7. $3.55
8. $2.50
9. $6.15
10. $6.40

Unit 4 - Fractions

Part 1: Halves and Quarters (pp. 52-53)

1. (a) B, D   (b) P, Q
2. (a) 2   (b) 4

Part 2: Writing Fractions (pp. 54-57)

    4, 5
1. (a) 1, 5   (b) 4, 5
2. (a) $\frac{1}{6}$ (b) 3, 8, $\frac{3}{8}$
3. (a) $\frac{3}{7}$ (b) $\frac{5}{6}$
4. (a) $\frac{4}{9}$ (b) $\frac{4}{6}$
    (c) $\frac{3}{8}$ (d) $\frac{7}{10}$
5. $\frac{1}{4}$
6. $\frac{1}{8}$, $\frac{1}{5}$, $\frac{1}{2}$
7. (a) $\frac{2}{5}$ (b) $\frac{6}{7}$ (c) $\frac{7}{9}$

Review B (p. 58)

1. (a) 833   (b) 300 (c) 479
2. (a) 505   (b) 101 (c) 127
3. (a) 24   (b) 50   (c) 24
4. (a) 4   (b) 9   (c) 9
5. 13 cm
6. $402
7. $15
8. 815 m
9. $2.55

Review C (p. 59)

1. (a) 562   (b) 397 (c) 448
2. (a) 269   (b) 231 (c) 19
3. (a) 35   (b) 90   (c) 32
4. (a) 9   (b) 5   (c) 6
5. (a) 208   (b) 530
    (c) 194   (d) 283
6. 35

7. 800
8. 9
9. 30 m
10. 24

Unit 5 - Time

Part 1: Telling Time (pp. 60-63)

1. (a) 5   (b) 30
    (c) 15   (d) 5
2. 6:00; 6:05; 6:20; 6:45; 7:15; 7:50

Part 2: Time Intervals (pp. 65-67)

1. (a) 25 minutes
    (b) 15 minutes
    (c) 25 minutes
    (d) 30 minutes
2. 60 minutes
3. (a) 25 minutes
    (b) 6 hours
4. 30 minutes
5. 8:35
6. 8:45

Practice 5A (p. 68)

1. (a) minutes (b) hours   (c) hours
    (d) minutes (e) hours
2. 40 minutes
3. 10:10

Review D (p. 69)

1. (a) 92   (b) 671 (c) 178
2. (a) 371   (b) 65 (c) 425
3. (a) 25   (b) 24 (c) 90
4. (a) 9   (b) 9   (c) 5
5. (a) $9   (b) $1.50   (c) $0.45
6. 9 m
7. (a) 189   (b) 20
8. $35
9. (a) $9.75   (b) $0.25

Unit 6 - Capacity

Part 1: Comparing Capacity (pp. 70-71)

1. 5, 3
2. B, A

Part 2: Liters (pp. 72-75)

1. The jug, the glass
2. 1 liter
3. (a) B   (b) 3 liters more
5. 4

Practice 6A (p. 76)

1. (a) A   (b) 4 liters more
2. 16 liters
3. 90 liters
4. 12 liters
5. 18 liters
6. 6

US Part 3: Gallons, Quarts, Pints and Cups (pp. 77-80)

2. the larger one on the left
3. quart
4. (a) no   (b) yes
5. (a) gallon   (b) pint, cup
   (c) cup, pint   (d) quart

Review E (US p. 81, 3d p. 77)

1. (a) 825   (b) 600   (c) 800
2. (a) 301   (b) 146   (c) 199
3. (a) 32   (b) 30   (c) 80
4. (a) 6   (b) 10   (c) 9
5. (a) $6.30 [$6.00]
   (b) $6.01   (c) $1.85
6. $7
7. $8.55
8. 35 liters
9. 11:20 a.m.
10. (a) 75   (b) 53

Unit 7 - Graphs

Part 1: Picture Graphs (US pp. 82-87, 3d pp. 78-83)

   4, 12, 6, 8, 4, 30
   (a) 2 fruit   (b) 12 fruit (c) 2
   (d) 4   (e) mango   (f) orange
1. (a) 15   (b) 12 (c) 5
   (d) zoo   (e) 9
2. (a) 8   (b) 24
   (c) US Carlos   3d Ahmad
   (d) 12   (e) 16
3. (a) 20   (b) 5
   (c) Goldfish (d) 35
   (e) $50   (f) $3

Review F (US p. 88, 3d p. 84)

1. (a) 809   (b) 788   (c) 841
2. (a) 203   (b) 38   (c) 77
3. (a) 10   (b) 24   (c) 60
4. (a) 7   (b) 6   (c) 3
5. 570 g
6. 288
7. 10 kg
8. 50 liters
9. (a) 397   (b) 892

Review G (US p. 89, 3d p. 85)

1. (a) 204   (b) 1000   (c) 510
2. (a) 109   (b) 208   (c) 48
3. (a) 18   (b) 12   (c) 40
4. (a) 4   (b) 4   (c) 7
5. 7
6. 65 liters
7. 16
8. 5:20 p.m.
9. $5.20
10. (a) 10   (b) 14

Unit 8 - Geometry

Part 1: Flat and Curved Faces (US pp. 90-92, 3d pp. 86-88)

1. (a) A   (b) C
   (c) D   (d) B

Part 2: Making Shapes (US pp. 93-99, 3d pp. 89-95)

4. (a) 4   (b) 6
6. (a) same as first figure
   (b) same as first figure
   (c) same as third figure
   (d) same as first figure
   (e) same as third figure
7. (a) same as third figure
   (b) same as third figure
   (c) same as first figure
   (d) same as first figure
   (e) same as third figure

Review H (US p. 100-101, 3d pp. 96-97)

1. (a) 825   (b) 300 (c) 541
2. (a) 160   (b) 159 (c) 303
3. (a) 16   (b) 70 (c) 28
4. (a) 8   (b) 6 (c) 10

5. (a) $10   (b) $1.81   (c) $1.50
6. (a) 18   (b) 15   (c) 2
    (d) 31   (e) 72   (f) 83
7. $\frac{2}{5}$
8. 8
9. 8:20 p.m.
10. 10
11. 240 g
12. 69
13. $1.75
14. $40
15. (a) $10   (b) $90
16. (a) 455   (b) 342

Unit 9 - Area

Part 1: Square Units (US pp. 102-105, 3d pp. 98-101)

    6
1. (a) 24   (b) 12   (c) 22
2. (a) 7   (b) 6   (c) 8
    (d) shape C (e) shape B
3. D and F
4. (a) 6   (b) 9
5. P - 7   Q - 8   R - 8   S - 12

Review I (US pp. 106-108, 3d pp. 102-108)

1. (a) 500   (b) 850   (c) 901
2. (a) 480   (b) 603   (c) 259
3. (a) 27   (b) 90   (c) 30
4. (a) 7   (b) 10   (c) 1
5. (a) $10   (b) $9.20   (c) $1.40
6. (a) 302   (b) 101
    (c) 566   (d) 225
7. (a) 70   (b) 200
    (c) 50   (d) 909
8. (a) 257, 275, 752
    (b) $\frac{1}{9}, \frac{1}{6}, \frac{1}{3}$
9. $2.15
10. 52 m

11. 10 hours
12. (a) 17   (b) 16   (c) A
13. 10 hours
14. 8
15. $1.80
16. 259
17. 153 liters
18. $6.00
19. (a) $535   (b) $1495
20. (a) 60   (b) 84

US Review J (pp. 109-112)

1. 4 in.
2. $21
3. 6
4. pencil; 1 in.
5. 331 qt
6. 77 gal
7. 46 lb
8. 6 yd
9. 12
10. 4
11. 9   8
12. (a) 12 c   (b) 14 c
13. $9
14. $27
15. 7 oz
16. 4 qt
17. 8 yd
18. (a) 11 oz   (b) 25 oz
19. 4 ft
20. 20 lb
21. check drawing
22. (a) 137 lb   (b) 196 lb
23. 7 qt
24. yes
25. 14 c
26. 74 in.
27. 720 yd
28. (a) 280 lb   (b) 62 lb
29. (a) 7   (b) 8
    (c) apple; 1 oz

Workbook Answer Key

Exercise 1

1. (a) 16   (b) 12 (c) 16
2. 20   70
    35   40
    45   30
    75   100
    80
    YOUR TEETH

Exercise 2

1. 10   70
    40   2
    95   85
2. (a) 1   (b) 5
    (c) 4   (d) 9
    (e) 20   (f) 65
    (g) 16   (h) 37
    (i) 58   (j) 42
    (k) 94   (l) 91
3. 80   90
    60   30
4. (a) 2   (b) 7
    (c) 15   (d) 73
    (e) 21   (f) 44
    (g) 78   (h) 66
    (i) 91   (j) 93
    (k) 99   (l) 96

Exercise 3

1. (a) 2   (b) 60   (c) 38
    (d) 40   (e) 80   (f) 27
2. (a) 27   (b) 58
    (c) 69   (d) 48
    (e) 88   (f) 79
    (g) 34   (h) 71
    (i) 28   (j) 80
    (k) 40   (l) 64
    (m) 51   (n) 97
    (o) 63   (p) 54
3. (a) 60   (b) 60
    (c) 90   (d) 70
    (e) 120   (f) 130
    (g) 130   (h) 130
    (i) 120   (j) 150
    (k) 140   (l) 180
4. (a) 45   (b) 68
    (c) 96   (d) 87
    (e) 103   (f) 109
    (g) 102   (h) 109

(i) 118   (j) 123
(k) 107   (l) 122

Exercise 4

1. (a) 166   (b) 235
    (c) 409   (d) 407
    (e) 788   (f) 659
2. (a) 141   (b) 196
    (c) 362   (d) 415
    (e) 572   (f) 664
    (g) 743   (h) 298
3. (a) 260   (b) 549
    (c) 482   (d) 658
    (e) 765   (f) 375
    (g) 677   (h) 893
4. (a) 310   (b) 500
    (c) 728   (d) 615
    (e) 466   (f) 955
    (g) 845   (h) 780
5. (a) 400   (b) 800
    (c) 900   (d) 500
    (e) 800   (f) 700
    (g) 600   (h) 900
6. (a) 450   (b) 706
    (c) 675   (d) 909
    (e) 864   (f) 525
    (g) 715   (h) 935

Exercise 5

1. (a) 70   (b) 4   (c) 89
2. (a) 70; 72 (b) 95; 99
    (c) 72; 75 (d) 94; 99
3. (a) 57   (b) 66
    (c) 87   (d) 48
    (e) 89   (f) 99

Exercise 6

1. 101   102   105
    101   104   105
2. (a) 136   (b) 152
    (c) 144   (d) 163

Exercise 7

1. (a) 282   (b) 344   (c) 298
    (d) 304   (e) 655   (f) 333
    (g) 507   (h) 497

Exercise 8

1. (a) 15   (b) 10   (c) 71
    (d) 13   (e) 50   (f) 32
2. (a) 21   (b) 64
    (c) 31   (d) 51
    (e) 72   (f) 91
    (g) 18   (h) 58
    (i) 78   (j) 46
    (k) 39   (l) 66
    (m) 46   (n) 28
    (o) 95   (p) 78
3. (a) 18   (b) 56
    (c) 65   (d) 43
    (e) 22   (f) 34
    (g) 71   (h) 87
4. (a) 10   (b) 20
    (c) 30   (d) 40
    (e) 10   (f) 10
    (g) 0   (h) 10
5. (a) 21   (b) 33
    (c) 27   (d) 18
    (e) 14   (f) 25
    (g) 59   (h) 12

Exercise 9

1. (a) 872   (b) 934   (c) 412
    (d) 262   (e) 103   (f) 653
2. (a) 442   (b) 678
    (c) 888   (d) 556
    (e) 228   (f) 944
    (g) 718   (h) 137
3. (a) 503   (b) 757
    (c) 121   (d) 327
    (e) 230   (f) 806
    (g) 632   (h) 428
4. (a) 469   (b) 658
    (c) 186   (d) 283
    (e) 377   (f) 545
    (g) 198   (h) 771
5. (a) 100   (b) 200
    (c) 700   (d) 200
    (e) 400   (f) 300
    (g) 100   (h) 300
6. (a) 433   (b) 89
    (c) 153   (d) 394
    (e) 235   (f) 227
    (g) 286   (h) 168

Exercise 10

1. (a) 2   (b) 80   (c) 52
2. (a) 48; 43   (b) 25; 21
    (c) 14; 11   (d) 28;22

3. (a) 42   (b) 12
    (c) 23   (d) 14
    (e) 21   (f) 25
4. (clockwise from top) 89; 55; 58; 98
5. (a) 23   (b) 89
    (c) 74   (d) 40
    (e) 22   (f) 89

Exercise 11

1. (a) 201   (b) 401   (c) 601
    (d) 701   (e) 302   (f) 502
    (g) 202   (h) 802

Exercise 12

1. (a) 81   (b) 203   (c) 457
    (d) 749   (e) 107   (f) 369
    (g) 682   (h) 534

Review 1

1. 769   405
    30   60
2. (a) 350   (b) 704
3. 90   56   500   680
    55   93   32   100
4. 879 → 889 → 897 → 978 → 987 → 990
5. 99 + 26 = 125; 125
6. $202
7. 180
8. $115
9. 450 g
10. 600 m

Exercise 13

1. 4, 8, 12, 16, 20, 24, 28, 32, 36, 40
2. (a) 4   (b) 8   (c) 12
    (d) 16   (e) 20
    (f) 24   (g) 28   (h) 32
    (i) 36   (j) 40

Exercise 14

1. (a) 8; 8   (b) 12; 12
    (c) 28; 28   (d) 36, 36

Exercise 15

1. (a) 12   (b) 24
    (c) 20   (d) 40
2. 16   32
    28   36
    20   28

Exercise 16

1. 2 x 4 = 8   9 x 4 = 36
    3 x 4 = 12   7 x 4 = 28
    6 x 4 = 24   5 x 4 = 20
    8 x 4 = 32   10 x 4 = 40
2. 4 x 5 = 20; 20
3. 24 cm
4. 12

Exercise 17

1. 8; 14; 15; 21; 18; 20; 32;
    18; 24; 10; 40; 9; 36; 24
2. 4 x 6 = 24
3. 27 m
4. 20 kg

Exercise 18

1. 1   2
    3   4, 4
    5, 5   6, 6
    10, 10   7, 7
    9, 9   8, 8
2. clockwise from top:
    32 ÷ 4 = 8; 20 ÷ 4 = 5; 36 ÷ 4 = 9;
    8 ÷ 4 = 2; 12 ÷ 4 = 3; 28 ÷ 4 = 7;
    16 ÷ 4 = 4; 24 ÷ 4 = 6
3. 9
4. $6
5. 7 m

Exercise 19

1. 5; 10; 15; 20; 25; 30; 35; 40; 45; 50

Exercise 20

1. 7 x 5 = 35   4 x 5 = 20
    5 x 3 = 15   10 x 5 = 50
    8 x 5 = 40   5 x 9 = 45
    5 x 6 = 30   1 x 5 = 5
    2 x 5 = 10   5 x 5 = 25
2. 30
3. 15
4. $40

Exercise 21

1. 1   2
    3   7, 7
    5, 5   9, 9
    4, 4   6, 6
    8, 8   10, 10

2. clockwise from pole:
    40 ÷ 5 = 8; 35 ÷ 5 = 7; 45 ÷ 5 = 9;
    20 ÷ 5 = 4; 50 ÷ 5 = 10; 25 ÷ 5 = 5;
    15 ÷ 5 = 3; 30 ÷ 5 = 6
3. 8
4. 10
5. $4

Exercise 22

1. 10; 20; 30; 40; 50; 60; 70; 80; 90; 100
2. 50   20   40
    30   32
    40   20   12
    35   50
3. 50
4. $100
5. $70

Exercise 23

1.   3
    5   5
    6   6
    7   7
    1   1
    3   3
    8   8
    4   4
    2   2
    9   9
2. 10 = 100 ÷ 10   7 = 70 ÷ 10
    2 = 20 ÷ 10   9 = 90 ÷ 9
    5 = 50 ÷ 10   8 = 80 ÷ 10
    6 = 60 ÷ 10   4 = 40 ÷ 10
3. 6 kg
4. $4
5. 9

Review 2

1. (a) 336   (b) 84
    (c) 584   (d) 206
    (e) 798   (f) 302
2. (a) 44; 300; 344; 344
    (b) 22; 40; 62; 62
3. (A) 12; 14; 5; 8
    (B) 27; 12; 6; 8
    (C) 32; 24; 5; 7
    (D) 25; 45; 6; 8
    (E) 30; 50; 6; 9
    (F) 30; 10; 10; 10
    (G) 18; 9; 7; 9
4. 20

5. 30
6. 8
7. $45
8. 36
9. 786

Exercise 24

1. $0.95; $0.59; $1.65; $1.56; $2.25
2. (a) $0.92 (b) $3.20 (c) $5.85 (d) $6.04 (e) $18.05
3. (a) $0.84 (b) $24.00 (c) $58.40 (d) $58.55

Exercise 25

1. 5 dollars 45 cents
   9 dollars 60 cents
   5 dollars 50 cents
   8 dollars
   4 dollars 40 cents
   6 dollars 90 cents
   85 cents
   4 dollars 5 cents
2. $3.05; $4.30; $5.00; $0.50; $9.75; $9.90
3. 6, 80 4, 65 0, 70 6, 45 7, 0

Exercise 26

1. $23.00 $4.00 $13.30
   $0.20 $7.50 $99.05
2. $0.15 $20.00 $47.00
   $74.50 $30.45 $86.05
   $47.15 $0.95 $95.05
   $40.25

Exercise 27

1. 180¢ 270¢ 345¢
   105¢ $0.10 $0.05
   $0.35 $3.00
2. $1.00 $2.05
   $2.00 $1.90
   $1.25 $3.50
   $2.40 $0.85
   $3.60 $0.70
   $4.05 $0.05
3. $0.30 10¢
   $0.45 75¢
   $1.20 105¢
   $2.50 305¢
   $3.00 250¢
   $0.75 150¢
   $3.45 400¢
   $0.06 8¢

Exercise 28

1. (a) $0.55 (b) $0.05 (c) $0.25 (d) $0.65
2. (clockwise from lower left)
   $0.15; $0.25; $0.20; $0.30; $0.35; $0.45

Exercise 29

1. (a) $0.80 (b) $1.60 (c) $7.40 (d) $6.90
2. (a) 50; 3.00; 3.50
   (b) 85, 7.00, 7.85
   (c) 5.30

Exercise 30

1. 55¢
2. $4.80
3. (a) $1.00 (b) 15¢ (c) $1.80 (d) $5.60 (e) bat, flying saucer

Exercise 31

1. (a) 4.85 (b) 4.45 (c) 10.05 (d) 13.70 (e) 2.55 (f) 1.90 (g) 2.75 (h) 3.80 (i) 4.00 (j) 3.00 (k) 5.00 (l) 5.00

Exercise 32

1. (a) 3.45; 3.75; 3.75
   (b) 5.60; 5.85; 5.85
   (c) 5.15; 5.80; 5.80
2. (a) $3.60 (b) $6.90 (c) $4.90 (d) $4.80 (e) $5.60 (f) $8.90

Exercise 33

1. E $3.05 F $5.45 L $3.55
   N $8.35 O $8.10 R $9.20
   S $6.20 U $6.00 W $9.10
   SUNFLOWER

Exercise 34

1. (a) $3.44 (b) $8.14 (c) $5.54 (d) $6.24
2. (a) $4.75 (b) $3.60 (c) $6.35 (d) $8.30

Exercise 35

1. (a) 1.85   (b) 4.45   (c) 3.05
   (d) 1.25   (e) 2.35   (f) 5.05
   (g) 6.00   (h) 9.15   (i) 3.20
   (j) 4.30   (k) 2.45   (l) 5.25

Exercise 36

1. (a) 4.80; 4.30; 4.30
   (b) 1.75; 1.40; 1.40
   (c) 2.90; 2.25; 2.25
2. (a) $3.60   (b) $3.25   (c) $2.15
   (d) $4.35   (e) $2.45   (f) $4.25

Exercise 37

1. A $1.65   D $2.55   F $4.75
   G $2.30   L $2.85   N $4.60
   O $2.60   R $0.45   Y $1.55
   DRAGONFLY

Exercise 38

1. (a) $3.31   (b) $2.46
   (c) $2.26   (d) $3.01
2. (a) $1.25   (b) $2.60
   (c) $0.15   (d) $2.30

Exercise 39

1. $5.65
2. $2.65
3. $2.05
4. $9.25
5. $3.55
6. $8.05

Review 3

1. (a) 451   (b) 960
2. (a) 999   (b) 700   (c) 908
3. (a) m   (b) cm
   (c) cm   (d) m
4. (a) kg   (b) g
   (c) g   (d) kg
5. (a) 1000   (b) 264
   (c) $5.90 (d) $2.80
   (e) $5.54 (f) $7.05
6. (a) 7, 7   (b) 8, 8
   (c) 9, 9   (d) 8, 8
7. 24
8. 4 m

9. $4.65
10. 785 g
11. 24 kg
12. $7.90

Review 4

1. (a) 6; 9; 18; 24
   (b) 20; 32; 36; 40
   (c) 15; 20; 30; 35
   (d) 30; 40; 50; 70; 90
2. (a) 405; 413
   (b) 596; 600
   (c) 402; 398
   (d) 866; 858
3. (a) 506   (b) 707
   (c) 802   (d) 394
4. (a) $0.40 (b) $0.80
   (c) $0.55 (d) $2.15
5. Bag A: $7.05   Bag B: $4.50
   $2.55
6. $9.00
7. $24.00
8. 9
9. 9
10. 35
11. 60

Exercise 40

1. First and second one of first row
   first and third one of second row.
2. First one of first row
   first, second and fourth one of second row.
5. (b) greater than [>]

Exercise 41

1. (a) $\frac{2}{3}$ (b) $\frac{5}{8}$
   (c) $\frac{7}{10}$ (d) $\frac{3}{4}$
2. (a) 1, 6   (b) 2, 5   (c) 1, 3
   (d) 3, 4   (e) 5, 8

Exercise 42

1. clockwise from left: $\frac{1}{9}$; $\frac{1}{2}$; $\frac{1}{12}$;
   $\frac{1}{6}$; $\frac{1}{10}$; $\frac{1}{4}$; $\frac{1}{8}$; $\frac{1}{3}$; $\frac{1}{5}$
2. clockwise from middle left: $\frac{7}{10}$; $\frac{5}{8}$;
   $\frac{3}{4}$; $\frac{2}{6}$; $\frac{3}{5}$; $\frac{5}{6}$; $\frac{2}{3}$; $\frac{3}{8}$

3. A $\dfrac{3}{4}$ C $\dfrac{2}{3}$ F $\dfrac{3}{5}$

    I $\dfrac{5}{6}$ O $\dfrac{1}{6}$ N $\dfrac{2}{5}$

    R $\dfrac{1}{2}$ S $\dfrac{5}{12}$ T $\dfrac{3}{8}$

    FRACTIONS

Exercise 44

2. (a) greater than [>]
    (b) less than [<]
    (c) less than [<]
    (d) greater than [>]
    (e) less than [<]
    (f) greater than [>]

3. (a) $\dfrac{1}{3}$ (b) $\dfrac{1}{4}$

    (c) $\dfrac{1}{9}$ (d) $\dfrac{1}{2}$

    (e) $\dfrac{1}{8}$ (f) $\dfrac{1}{4}$

4. (a) $\dfrac{1}{6}$ (b) $\dfrac{1}{10}$

    (c) $\dfrac{1}{5}$ (d) $\dfrac{1}{12}$

    (e) $\dfrac{1}{10}$ (f) $\dfrac{1}{9}$

5. (a) $\dfrac{1}{2}$ (b) $\dfrac{1}{5}$

    (c) $\dfrac{1}{4}$ (d) $\dfrac{1}{5}$

6. (a) $\dfrac{1}{7}$ (b) $\dfrac{1}{12}$

    (c) $\dfrac{1}{4}$ (d) $\dfrac{1}{9}$

7. $\dfrac{1}{10},\ \dfrac{1}{8},\ \dfrac{1}{4},\ \dfrac{1}{2}$

8. $\dfrac{1}{3},\ \dfrac{1}{5},\ \dfrac{1}{9},\ \dfrac{1}{12}$

Exercise 45

1. (a) $\dfrac{2}{3}$ (b) $\dfrac{6}{8}$

    (c) $\dfrac{3}{5}$ (d) $\dfrac{5}{6}$

2. clockwise from left:
    $\dfrac{1}{3};\ \dfrac{5}{8};\ \dfrac{1}{6};\ \dfrac{1}{4};\ \dfrac{2}{5};\ \dfrac{1}{12}$

Exercise 46

1. clockwise from top: 0; 5; 10; 15;
    20; 25; 30; 35; 40; 45; 50; 55
    50
2. (b) 5; 4:00; 4:15
    (c) 35; 10:00; 10:35
3. 3:25   12:35
    6:00   8:55
    2:20   9:05
    12:30   11:00
4. 7:30   8:15   1:30
    5:05   11:40   9:10
    1:20   8:50   12:45
    4:25   6:40   9:50

Exercise 47

1. (a) 5; 3; 5; 3
    (b) 25; 12; 25; 12
    (c) 20; 3; 20; 3
    (d) 10; 5; 10; 5
2. (a) 10; 6   (b) 15; 7
    (c) 15; 7   (d) 25; 8
3.

Exercise 48

1. (a) 20   (b) 15
    (c) 25   (d) 40
2. (a) 1   (b) 4
    (c) 3   (d) 4
3. (a) 15   (b) 35
    (c) 35   (d) 50
4. (a) 4:05; 5; 4:10
    (b) 2:50; 10; 3:00
    (c) 9:30; 40; 10:10
    (d) 5:45; 7; 12:45

Exercise 49

1. (a) 4:35 a.m.   (b) 11:50 p.m.
   (c) 6:15 a.m.   (d) 6:00 p.m.
   (e) 3:15 a.m.
2. (a) 5:25 p.m.   (b) 4:15 a.m.
   (c) 1:40 p.m.   (d) 12:10 a.m.
   (e) 2:55 a.m.

Review 5

1. (a) 569   (b) 700
   (c) 444   (d) 300
2. (a) 40   (b) 16
   (c) 826   (d) 704
3. clockwise from top: 200; 35; 7;
   70; 160.   Middle: 63
4. (a) $9.00   (b) $6.40
   (c) $3.35   (d) $3.10
5. (a) less than   [<]
   (b) greater than [>]
   (c) equal to   [=]
   (d) greater than [>]
6. (a) 36   (b) 9
   (c) 40   (d) 8
7. 2
8. (a) $12.40   (b) $27.40
9. 45
10. 5
11. 498

Exercise 51

1. A; B
2. A; B
3. B
4. X
5. (a) B; A   (b) 2; 2

Exercise 53

1. (a) 4   (b) 4
2. (c) 3   (b) 3
US 3. 142 liters
US 4. 20 liters
3d 3. *(a) 7*   *(b) 7*
3d 4. *(a) 5*   *(b) 5*

US Exercise 54

1. 145 gallons
2. 2 quarts
3. (a) 7   (b) 7
4. (a) 5   (b) 5

3d *Exercise 54*

1. *142 ℓ*
2. *145 ℓ*
3. *20 ℓ*
4. *2 ℓ*

Exercise 55

1. (a) 3   (b) 6   (c) 2
   (d) Red   (e) Yellow
2. (a) 8   (b) 5   (c) 5
   (d) 3
   (e) US Cameron 3d *Chengfa*

Exercise 56

1. (a) 10   (b) 14   (c) 4
   (d) 6   (e) 6

Exercise 57

1. (a) 10   (b) 30   (c) 12
2. (a) color 5 squares
   (b) color 6 triangles
3. (a) $9   (b) June   (c) May
   (d) $9   (e) $30

Exercise 58

1. (a) 50
   (b) US Matthew 3d *Minghua*
   (c) US Annie   3d *Aihua*
   (d) 10   (e) 30   (f) 70
2. (a) no   (b) yes   (c) no
   (d) yes   (d) no

Exercise 59

3. (a) rectangle
   (b) circle
   (c) square
   (d) triangle
   (e) rectangle
   (f) rectangle
4. (a) A 1, 1
   B 5, 0
   C 6, 0
   D 2, 1
   E   6, 0
   (b) 2   (c) 2   (d) 2

Exercise 60

1. first → third   second → fourth
   third → second   fourth → first
2. first → second   second → fourth
   third → first   fourth → third

Exercise 61

1. Answers can vary
   (b)

   (c) 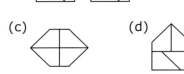   (d)

Exercise 62

1. (a) half circle, triangle
   (b) triangle, square
   (c) half circle, quarter circle
   (d) square, rectangle
   (e) quarter circle, rectangle
2. Answer can vary.
   (b) 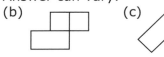   (c)

   (d)    (e)

Exercise 64

1. (a)   (b)

   (c)   (d)

2. (a)   (b)   (c)

   (d) 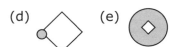   (e)

Review 6

1. 18   40   36   90
   9   8   8   10
2. (a) five dollars and ninety cents
   (b) nine dollars and fifty cents
   (c) five dollars and nine cents
   (d) nine dollars and five cents
3. $\frac{2}{3}, \frac{3}{4}, \frac{5}{6}$
4. (a) 5   (b) 3
5. (a) 10   (b) 30
6. $3.20
7. $6.05
8. $7
9. 65
10. $24.00
11. $310.00

Exercise 65

1. (a) same   (b) different
   (c) same   (d) same
   (e) same
2. (a) first   (b) first   (c) first
   (d) second   (e) first

Exercise 66

1. second → first
   third → fifth
   fourth → third
   fifth → fourth
2. (a) 8   (b) 5
   (c) 7   (d) 11
   (e) 9   (f) 16

Exercise 67

2. (a) A: 6
      B: 5
      C: 6
      D: 7
   (b) D   (c) B   (d) A, C

Review 7

1. (a) 408   (b) 250
2. (a) 950   (b) 728   (c) 972
   (d) 620   (e) 590
3. (a) 59   (b) 42
   (c) 37   (d) 76

4. (a) 150   (b) 300
    (c) 500   (d) 841
    (e) 396   (f) 549
    (g) 625   (h) 73
5. (a) equal to [=]
    (b) less than [<]
6. (a)   (b)

7. A, F, J, H   C, I , E   B, D, G
8. (a) 205   (b) 325   (c) 290
9. 270
10. 8
11. 45 m
12. $1.70
13. 60 liters
14. 8

Review 8

1. (a) 8, 10, 12, 14, 16, 18, 20
    (b) 12, 15, 18, 21, 24, 27, 30
    (c) 16, 20, 24, 28, 32, 36, 40
    (d) 20, 25, 30, 35, 40, 45, 50
    (e) 40, 50, 60, 70, 80, 90, 100

2. (a) ℓ (b) min   (c) m
    (d) g   (e) kg   (f) h
    (g) cm   (h) g
4. (a) 6   (b) 5   (c) A, B
5. (a) half circle, triangle
    (b) rectangle, square
6. (a) 58, 340, 403, 900
    (b) $\frac{1}{2}$, $\frac{1}{7}$, $\frac{1}{4}$, $\frac{1}{2}$
7. (a) 20   (b) 5   (c) 30
8. 165
9. $7
10. $5
11. 64
12. $6.45
13. 32 liters
14. $1.30
15. US 12 gal   3d ℓ
16. $3.40
US 17. 8
US 18. 42
US 19. $4.30
US 20. yes
US 21. 21
US 22. 9.53